50 ANSWERS
CAREGIVER CHALLENGES

Coping with
STROKE

Monica Vest Wheeler

ISBN 978-0-9759875-7-5

A portion of the proceeds from the sale of this book will be donated to Retreat & Refresh Stroke Camp™. Please consider making a contribution to this non-profit organization:

Retreat & Refresh Stroke Camp™
425 Giles Lane, Peoria, IL 61614
1-866-688-5450
www.strokecamp.org

info@strokecamp.org

Contact Turning Empathy into Action to find out how you can sell this book as a fundraiser for your organization or to buy in bulk.

Turning Empathy into Action
P.O. Box 276, Peoria, IL 61650-0276
Toll-free 877-267-4640 (877-COPING-0)
info@copeandsurvive.com

Contact us online and order additional books at:
www.strokecopebook.com or www.monicavestwheeler.com

3

Inside

Introduction	4	Empathy	51	Needs	90
Hope	7	Inward	54	Acceptance	93
Fear	11	Grief	56	Routine	95
Self	14	Listen	59	Choices	97
Denial	18	Ask	61	Social	99
Overload	20	Engaged	64	Flexibility	101
Reconnection	22	Forward	66	Reasons	104
Look	24	Summarize	68	Familiarity	106
Timing	28	Vocabulary	70	Technology	109
Help	30	Tough	72	Protective	111
Abandonment	33	Humor	74	Victory	115
Imperfection	36	Repeat	76	Zip	117
Differences	39	Investment	77	Junk	118
Fire	41	Classroom	79	Motivation	121
Reality	43	Checklist	82	Positive	124
Anger	45	Recognition	84	Resources	127
Emotions	49	Discovery	86	Author page	128
Depression	50	Purpose	88		

All those complex emotions of being a stroke caregiver

"To see what I see, you've got to be where I am."

That's one of the most accurate and straight-forward descriptions you'll ever hear or read about living life with stroke, as the survivor *or* the caregiver. This compact volume is filled with the best and most practical first-hand quotes, insights and tips you'll ever find on coping with the everyday emotional challenges of stroke as a caregiver, because every word of it is real *and* common sense.

This book meets you where *you* are, no matter where you are in time.

While the story of one survivor and/or caregiver can be extraordinarily moving, *real life* demands that you educate yourself in many classrooms to stretch your imagination and discover new resources and be reminded that *you are not alone*. Because every stroke and individual is different, you need to glean the perspective of hundreds of survivors and caregivers to bring the diverse realities of stroke into closer focus.

That's what you'll find neatly packaged here, snippets of one experience, then another and yet another that you can piece together to make sense of how *you* can best cope with this complex puzzle called stroke. This brain attack has peaks and valleys so ridiculously high and low that this roller-coaster can flip the strongest stomach, heart and mind without warning.

Yes, there are physical challenges with stroke, but the emotional exercises can be as or more brutal for both survivor and caregiver. Emotions are often overlooked because the world often only digests, comprehends and responds to what it can *see* … such as the loss of the use of a limb or confinement to a wheelchair, which are common stroke side effects.

However, we cannot see the other pain within the brain that can plague both survivor *and* caregiver … the grief in facing the loss of abilities, the destruction of firmly rooted dreams and finely crafted plans, disappearing friends and family members, and the unexpected changes within the survivor *and* caregiver as they struggle with this brain attack.

We fear most what we cannot see with our own eyes. We are frightened by an unexplained noise behind us, but are calmed when we turn and see its innocent source. We fear what we cannot see happening in the human brain, when the survivor looks perfectly "normal" but behaves in ways that are not "normal" for them or most people.

That's why we must get "inside."

Stroke creates a whole new world for everyone touched by it. It's up to each individual on how that new world looks, feels and moves. You, as a caregiver, carry much responsibility in this constant whirlwind of emotions by maintaining a focus on love, compassion, empathy, patience, common sense, physical stamina, and heavy doses of tough love. You're going to need them all and much more.

Indulge in these words of wisdom, advice and unique insights as you continue to adjust to your life as a caregiver. Stop to reflect on the short sections entitled "Little BIG insight," which feature brief statements about the everyday realities of stroke. The "Caregiver insight" offers direct quotes from caregivers around the country who *do* understand the complex emotions that come with the title you now share with them.

You are not alone. Period.

You'll also find "Survivor insight" because it's *very* important for caregivers to peer inside the world of survivors and their struggles and successes. These can bolster your understanding and patience as a caregiver. Any of these tidbits can be the starting point for an important conversation with your survivor, as communication, in one form or another, can make or break your relationship. (I've also created a book for survivors so they can glimpse into what you caregivers go through!)

Along the way, capture what helps so *you* can share with another future caregiver in need … as long as you remember that what works for one may not always work for another. It will also serve as a healthy reminder later that *you* have "survived" the stroke, too.

Hope

The male survivor shakes his head as he explains, "The doc said, *'I didn't expect you to be here this morning.'*"

Well, that's a nice way to wake up to a new day *and* life!

While multitudes of survivors and caregivers are *extremely* grateful for and indebted to the outstanding medical expertise applied in the emergency phase of stroke care, there are many who are dismayed by the dismal words uttered by healthcare professionals at the onset.

"When we were told there was no hope," says a survivor, "I was expected to go home and die." He's regained far more physical abilities than anyone could have predicted.

A caregiver says, "I can't believe anyone would tell a stroke survivor they would never be able to do something again. They're just plain ignorant! That would be horrible! That's mean!"

Here's the official scoop, according to another caregiver:

"Medical people don't always know everything."

Ah, now there's *the* truth!

The medical community is *very* knowledgeable about many intricacies of the human body, but when it comes to the brain, *no human being* has all the answers. (At least as of the publication date of this volume; check back in future editions.)

Seriously, *no one*, repeat, *no one*, knows *exactly* how a patient will fare in the short and long term after a stroke. Even the most sophisticated imaging equipment, that can peer deep within the most powerful organ in the world, is *not* a crystal ball in disguise.

However, being overly pessimistic *or* optimistic, or offering zero hope should probably be outlawed. Survivors and caregivers have heard it *all:* will never walk or talk again, will be back to "normal" and work in no time at all, will never make any more progress after six months or one year, etc. etc. etc. And then the opposite or nothing or everything happens.

People have this deep need for immediate solutions and/or answers in crises. It's natural. It's one of the pains of being human.

"I told the doctors this from the beginning," says a caregiver. " *'Please tell me the absolute facts. Will she ever walk? Is she going to be disabled the rest of her life?'* "

Well, we know you want answers *NOW*, because the love of your life is fighting for her life, but no responsible medical professional can *or* should say that first day or week if she'll ever walk or if she'll be disabled the rest of her life. Stroke's individual impact is totally unpredictable.

Families don't want candy-coated or sanitized medical information or news; they want and need the truth as it unfolds. And that takes time as the actual damage to the brain often *s-l-o-w-l-y* reveals itself after the subsiding of dangerous initial swelling.

Whether caused by clots, bleeds or bursts, stroke is a *very* serious brain injury, and those cells not destroyed at the start are scrambling to recover from this catastrophic assault. It's like the aftermath of an earthquake: the surviving cells are running into broken and blocked roads and have to find or create new pathways to civilization to stay alive.

Medical professionals need to acknowledge that they don't know what will happen in an hour, tomorrow or next year. The best they can honestly offer is "this *could* or *could not* happen."

While they must be vigilant, families need to accept the painful reality that *nothing* is certain. If nothing is certain in life, other than death and taxes, then there is certainly no certainty about how a damaged human brain will respond after stroke. A brain attack can strike two people in the exact same region of the brain, but the outcomes can be completely different. Why? No one has the exact answer other than every human being and situation is different.

And that's what makes stroke so frustrating.

The key for loved ones is being realistic and digesting a *lot* of brain education quickly. The primary lesson? While we've learned much about the brain, there is far more that we do not know nor can begin to understand at this point in human history.

Remember: *every brain is different.* Some survivors make miraculous recoveries while others struggle with basic activities of daily living (ADL) the rest of their lives. No one can predict how the individual human brain will rewire or rebuild itself, if at all. And there are always exceptions to the "rules."

One caregiver notes, "You always have to have hope."

Hope, that's what has carried humanity to this point, and it's what *will* lift you through the earliest and toughest days of a loved one's stroke.

Little BIG insight

▸ Stroke is a lifelong recovery process.

▸ Find a part of a song that speaks to your heart. Keep singing it.

▸ Walk through doors that open even when you're not sure what lies beyond.

▸ Most people will rise to the occasion if you give them the opportunity.

II

Fear

"They're scared," says a caregiver.

Darn right that survivors are scared! Their body is not cooperating the way it always has. Lifelong voluntary and involuntary movements were "no-brainers." Now they're not. Before the stroke, thoughts were automatically transmitted into action. They walked and talked without having to think about every step and word.

They may not comprehend what everyone is saying in the rush of the stroke's immediate aftermath. Brain cells that specialized in translating sound waves into recognizable words may have been bounced around. Imagine finding yourself in that crowd at the Tower of Babel.

And besides, there are often too many voices surrounding the survivor at the same time to pick them apart!

Of course they're scared with all they could face in those first days … the sudden loss or interruption of communication skills … the strange and noisy hospital environment … the pokes, prods and pain in parts of their body they didn't even know existed before this attack … all these trained strangers whirling around them and stealing their privacy … the claustrophobic feel of being confined to bed … the inability to move possibly half of their body … being told to cooperate, focus and move, repeat … and so many other converging emotions and sensations.

And don't forget the fear of dying, leaving loved ones behind and a lengthy list of shoulda-coulda-woulda …

Words of support, love and faith, and human touch are vital anchors in keeping survivors connected with their "real" world amid all this initial chaos. They're slowly discovering what is different about their bodies, what works and what doesn't, and even then, it's darn confusing because that could all change in the next hour or day. They need reassurances that, while there is much to be tackled during this recovery, they won't be "going it" alone.

Consider these ways to engage your survivor:

▸ They need familiar voices, music, images and scents as healthy distractions, though none should be overpowering.

▸ If you have a soft voice, you may need to learn to speak up. If you're too loud, you may need to learn to reduce the volume. Don't take it too personally if they ask you to keep repeating something or to "shut up."

▸ While engaging in conversation, maintain eye contact. This also reassures them that you are focused on *them*.

▶ Immediately create a display of photos that survivors can point to if they have difficulty speaking or are experiencing some short-term memory loss. Include not only loved ones and friends, but images of pets, rooms at home, cars, front and back yards, and other scenes that can help trigger recognition and offer a way to communicate.

▶ Have children and/or grandchildren design colorful get-well drawings and post them in prominent places for easy viewing.

▶ Put together a picture sheet of their favorite foods to ease meal selection and provide homework reciting their names. These are excellent resources for the speech therapists to better assist your loved one.

Remember, you're part of the therapy team now. Listen, learn and practice, practice, practice! You can and *will* earn that captain's cap!

Caregiver insight

▶ "You're so lost those first few days."

▶ "You've got to be bossy. I'm not afraid to say what I've got to say to the doctors."

▶ "I thought only old people had strokes. Not so."

Self

Look in the mirror. You're scared, too, even if you think you're hiding it well from the patient and the rest of the world. It's okay to admit that you're terrified of losing your loved one or "parts" of them.

Stroke happens not only to the patient, but the *entire* family as it rattles the foundation. Your adrenaline is working overtime, often without adequate fuel, namely sleep and "good" nourishment.

Give yourself frequent breaks during those intense early days. It's a good habit to develop early on. You need some rest to be at your best for your survivor. If they see you at the brink of exhaustion all the time, that creates more anxiety that they don't need.

That doesn't mean "faking it." It means, ask the hospital staff if there is a place where you could grab a nap or shower. More medical centers are or should be offering break rooms for families to freshen up, yet still be close by. Even 20 minutes away from the bedside could be the fuel that gets you through the rest of the day.

Looking back at the immediate crisis of stroke, one caregiver says she and her two teens should have had fresh and healthy food to sustain them at the most basic level.

While she was at the hospital with her husband for 15 hours a day, their kids ate junk or not much at all at home because they were under serious stress, too. There was no fresh fruit in the house because she had no time to go to the store. She could only sleep and start the draining routine all over again.

She knows *now* that she should have asked for specific things when people offered assistance. It's not all that unusual that friends and family feel helpless and may not utilize some much needed common sense about how everyday life continues even when somebody's world is falling apart.

There's often an avalanche of chaotic assistance in the beginning as everyone rushes in out of a sincere desire to do *something*. You don't want to turn anyone down but may not know how or what to ask and/or accept. You *have* to take a few minutes to break down your everyday life and responsibilities and how those can be delegated and/or postponed.

▸ You need a trusted and understanding family member or friend to be a team leader, to coordinate calling, email or texting trees, to draft a meal schedule that provides consistency without repetition, to make *you* sit down and offer valuable input on the process. It *will* save you time and frustration.

▸ Make a list of things or services people could provide, laminate it if possible, and put it in a prominent place so you can refer to it when you're unsure how to answer an offer.

▸ Space out assistance so that it doesn't overwhelm your family with too much food and/or help one week and none the following.

▸ Remember your favorite foods that would make you feel better physically and emotionally.

▸ Pre-bagging fresh fruit, healthy snacks and a favorite beverage can save considerable time and money in the hospital environment or help avoid an unhealthy habit of eating out all the time.

▸ Remember, it's the simplest foods, gestures and opportunities that will sustain a caregiver's and family's strength as you all move into whole new roles, relationships and realities.

A caregiver who is not eating or sleeping properly won't be at the level of efficiency they need to be to provide the best care for the survivor. You're not being selfish; you're being smart. That's how *you're* going to survive *their* stroke.

" *J*ust remember that each survivor is an individual. Do not assume that because they cannot talk to you by speech that they don't need help. Pay attention to the body language and the eye movement. These talk volumes if you will take the time to listen. We must learn to listen."

Caregiver

▸ "My dad was a busy surgeon, and being that he is single and my brother is overseas, I have become his 'team leader' (not sure what else to call myself). Coping might be the only thing we are both doing right now, but we are lucky his stroke was not worse. I have faith he can get back to his baseline with dedicated motivation from all. I do have great family and friends around, but for multiple reasons have taken the care of my dad on myself. I think it is hard for me to ask for help. Finding the right people to help takes more energy then I have and I have learned that in some ways creates more work." *Caregiver*

Denial

"You're still in denial in the hospital," says a survivor. "You're not ready to meet someone else who's had a stroke."

Many survivors and caregivers have echoed that same sentiment. However, quite a few now wish they had met another long-term survivor or caregiver early on to reassure them that there is hope and that they are not alone.

That sense of loneliness can be intense in those early hours, days and weeks. Though you, the caregiver, have been through the drills and attended "Stroke 101" class condensed into an insanely short period of time, it's quite scary when you have to do it yourself.

Denial can be a nasty companion in the beginning: "We'll wake up tomorrow, and this nightmare will be over. My survivor will be back to what they were doing, and so will I. This isn't going to inconvenience our lives for too long …"

Stroke is *so* rude and inconsiderate. It drops in unannounced, rattles a lot of nerves, costs a lot of money and is terribly demanding. Stroke will likely be part of your lives for a very long time, but it doesn't have to *control* every aspect of your life.

The longer you hold on to denial, the more difficult the transition to a caregiving role will be. You then might search for every excuse in the world why you'll never be successful, or likely focus on the more negative, "I'm a failure." You'll waste a lot of your own brain power convincing yourself that you're not "smart enough" to coordinate the survivor's care.

Or some caregivers go the other extreme at first, "Oh, this will be a breeze. I can do anything *and* everything." Then things don't go perfectly, and the walls shake around them.

Just chill. You *will* be okay. Make that decision *now*.

Little BIG insight

▶ Don't hide behind stroke.

▶ Acceptance, *not resignation*, is gradual; you can't process it immediately. You adjust to the news hour by hour, day by day.

▶ Don't be embarrassed by stroke. It's a brain *injury*.

▶ You cannot wait to do the things you want to do with your life.

▶ Think creatively about the things you do on an everyday basis.

Overload

<u>A stroke changes *everything* in an instant.</u>

Families need an abundance of information about stroke, yet they can't absorb it all at once. It's humanly impossible! Caregivers often don't know what to ask or pay attention to in the beginning.

The non-stop information first thrown at you is simply too much to grasp at one, two or even three sittings. You need a continuous, long-term stream of oral and written sustenance, *not* lectures.

"I was *so* hungry for information," says a female caregiver. "If somebody, a counselor or nurse, would have called me later, I'd have known what questions to ask. At first, I didn't. I was on my own. I had nobody to talk to. They gave me stuff at discharge, but it meant nothing to me at the time. I thought I had to buy equipment. Then I find out I could rent something for a couple of months, like a potty chair. All these little things."

Understanding more about all these "little things" can save you some really big headaches and bucks down the road. When survivor and caregiver finally go home and the front door closes, it can be the most intense moment of isolation, emptiness and loss that you can imagine.

Caregivers *and* survivors need follow-up calls and messages to get through the toughest, loneliest days. It's reasonable to ask yourself, "What can I do to be the best I can given the circumstances?" However, it's a little hard to make plans when you're not sure what the next hour will bring, but that's the way of stroke.

You, as the caregiver, need to prepare an ongoing list of questions, concerns and frustrations to share with doctors, nurses and therapists. You need to toss aside the natural, yet annoying, fear of asking for answers and assistance. These folks are there to help *you*!

The oft-used statement, "it takes a village to raise a child," needs a twist when it comes to stroke: "It takes a village to care for a stroke survivor *and* caregiver." It also takes a world of understanding and patience to make strides against a broken brain, the damage a stroke can leave behind.

Lighten your load by keeping *only* the essentials you need at the time.

Survivor insight

▸ "Learn to teach people about stroke by example."

▸ "Be assertive, ask what we need, slow down, listen to me."

▸ "I just want someone to tell me what's wrong and how to fix it."

Reconnection

"My sister hadn't spoken to Mom for years, and she shows up at the hospital," says a caregiver. "Now my sister is back in Mom's life. Unfortunately, it took that tragedy to wake her up. It's the only good thing that has come out of it."

Life or death situations, such as stroke, can have an amazing or startling impact on people. There are countless stories of how families have mended after tragic events. Sometimes that's the only way some people can understand the fragility of life, when it nearly ends.

However, some reconnections may still need mending when the initial crisis is over. The folks who have come back into the picture shouldn't ask the survivor or you, the caregiver, to take on that responsibility at the start. Yes, there may have been a terrible wrong at some point on the part of one or both parties, but those may have to be forgiven and/or forgotten to move forward and reunite a family.

Hmm, what if it's *you* who's holding a grudge?

Well, you can continue to let it steal your life and/or destroy your happiness. Then you'll be in "fine" shape to care for the survivor. Or it just may kill you, leaving your survivor all alone or in a real mess.

Decisions, decisions …

Sometimes we have to move on in life. Many disagreements arise over something so minor or senseless in comparison to the challenges of stroke and "the big picture" of life. Those who focus on negatives will find themselves lonely, empty and trapped in the past. Some folks would prefer to die before apologizing or forgiving. Just a little selfish, you think?

Can you change them? Probably not. But we can change *ourselves*. Sometimes we simply have to walk away from family members who are poisoning *our* lives. Remember the good times, hold those memories dear, but let go of the negativity or anger. Your emotional well-being may be one step from disintegrating because of the demands of stroke caregiving, and while it's terrible to say it, some people are not worth the emotional turmoil they inflict. Grieve and move on like any other loss in life. You *can* emerge stronger because of it.

If wounds are healed by stroke, be grateful for that miracle, but focus as a family on the survivor's rehabilitation and new life. Find ways to mend broken relationships without demanding something else untangible in return, especially of a stroke patient who is focused on surviving.

Life is too precious. *Get over it!* You *will* feel and do better!

Look

The female survivor shakes her head at the memory.

"When I was first at the hospital, I got frustrated because I was trying to tell this nurse to get something. I got upset. She told me, *'Don't get mad at me because you can't talk and I can't understand you.'* "

Fortunately this survivor had a roommate, an "angel," who understood her and could interpret her needs to the nursing staff.

Hmm, just slightly rude, and talk about kicking you while you're down. Okay, we'll give her a break. Maybe *she* was having a bad day. But survivors are experiencing a string of *really* bad days. Self-confidence, self-worth, self-esteem, etc., are badly eroded or damaged in the aftermath of stroke. They're still in shock and devastated at what their body has done to them. They may already feel like a burden on family, friends and society as a whole, but they've just been punched in the gut again by someone who is a professional healthcare provider, who is supposed to be compassionate.

What would you, as her caregiver, have done if you had witnessed that scene? Would you have chewed 'em up and spit 'em out? Ran out into the hall looking for their supervisor and complained loudly enough for everyone to hear?

How about option three: work with the staff to make life easier for everyone, especially the survivor?

▸ How about offering a notepad or ABC board to point to letters or a picture sheet for most common needs during a hospital stay?

▸ How about paying attention to body language? When it comes to stroke, talking may be preferred, but it may not be possible.

▸ How about asking another staff member to help "interpret"?

Someone may need to be in the hospital during normal waking hours to advocate for their loved one, especially if their speech has been affected. Many caregivers report they saw other patients "fall through the cracks" because no one was there to speak for them. For example, some patients sat in soiled clothing longer than acceptable. Caregivers grew to trust some staff but not others because of the huge flow of people in and out of the patient's room. Every case is different, and honestly, hospital employees can't do everything because of increased demands, emergencies and staff shortages.

The above story has a "happy" ending, the survivor says.

"The same nurse later told me, *'Do you remember when I told you not to get mad at me because I couldn't understand you?'* She apologized. I told her I didn't hold grudges. She was very helpful later on when she saw I was trying. A lot of the nurses and therapists said they wished they had more patients like me, more cooperative. I wanted to get well."

As a caregiver, you're now part of the medical system and will be for a long time. Patients will get a more enthusiastic response from healthcare providers when they give their best effort at therapy. That's true in any life situation. What we give, we get back manyfold. Supportive, cooperative caregivers are an added bonus all the way around.

Healthcare providers may need gentle reminders that the survivor is only trying to tell the world, "I'm not stupid. I just can't get the words out." Because every patient is different, *they're* still learning something new about stroke every day, too. Add subtle teaching to *your* resumé!

Little BIG insight

▸ Ask the survivor their opinion and give them time to reply or discuss.

▸ As a survivor works to regain motor skills, perhaps they can do what most of us consider mundane, yet can be therapeutic for them, such as sorting small items like coins, buttons, or items by color.

▸ Conversation with a survivor can shift *very* quickly because of the brain injury, and they may not even notice it.

▶ "Our daughters decided that I needed a break (whew!) and they arranged for me to be gone for a week. They each took two days off work and shared the weekend. The last day I hired a caregiver. I had an absolutely wonderful time. My youngest daughter made me feel so good. She whispered in my ear, 'Mom, I have new-found respect for you.' She couldn't have said anything that would have made me happier!" *Caregiver*

"I have no children and now am caring for Mom. That's God's way of joking, 'You're not going to get out of it. You're going to care for some-body, you silly girl, you.' I was so angry, so angry. But I don't want to have a stroke."

Caregiver

Timing

A survivor recounts her frustration in dealing with the initial demands of therapy, trying to get an uncooperative body to function again.

"They sent a speech therapist in the hospital. What I did was exasperating because she would come the latter part of the day when I was tired, and I really was not caring whether I talked or not. Later when I was in the rehab unit, I would be delighted to try to form my words, but in the hospital I didn't care."

Though she initially regained many physical skills, she still struggled with cognition.

"The TV, I didn't have a clue. It was just noise at first. I couldn't follow a storyline at all, and reading I couldn't understand. My husband would have the TV on, and a program maybe wouldn't interest me, but I thought, well, I will listen to it. Sometimes I would understand it."

Stroke recovery is all about timing, and for every survivor, it depends on a different clock. That's what makes planning so difficult for you as a caregiver and in some cases, impossible, because no one knows, not even the survivor, how their energy will hold up on a daily basis, especially early on as the brain begins its recovery process. We need to set our survivor up for success, not failure.

However, the reality and dictates of therapy and insurance do make it harder to accommodate the unique needs of survivors. Some patients are gung ho in the morning while others cannot focus on anything. *It's the brain injury!* That's often hard for a caregiver to accept when they're sure laziness or stubbornness is the culprit.

There are going to be days when nothing makes sense, and other moments of "eureka!" when a skill suddenly returns. *Take the time to celebrate!* That's why the little things in life can often mean the most to a survivor … like figuring out the killer in the murder mystery all by themselves.

Little BIG insight

▸ The public isn't generally aware of cognitive challenges with stroke. They only think of it as involving speech problems or paralysis.

▸ Survivors may be on their best "behavior" during therapy and not exhibit the frustration or stubbornness they "share" at home.

▸ Survivors have to have a lot of patience, too, because they may be doing things they don't want to do, even though they know it will help.

Help

"Outside of my kids," says a caregiver, "I've never had any help."

Caregivers quickly find out if their family, particularly adult children, will help or ignore them.

Some family members only visit to do chores or run errands and don't want a close relationship with the survivor, most often to distance themselves emotionally. Sadly, they don't want to see how "damaged" the survivor is now.

Unfortunately, they've given up far too soon.

One woman has witnessed extremes in her children. Her youngest daughter has been a "Godsend" in caring for her father. The oldest child used to be very close to his dad, but now, "He can't stand to see him the way he is. He wants to remember him the way he *was*. We never see him."

Another says, "They don't realize how hurtful it is," when family seems to vanish after the initial strike of stroke.

Facing the absence of loved ones can be as or more painful and depressing than addressing a stroke's physical challenges. The lack of visits, calls, letters, emails — whatever mode of communication possible and preferred — becomes more noticeable after the immediate weeks following the emergency. That's when you and your survivor likely have your first chance to breathe and look around at what's the same and different. That's when you'll see and search for your support network, who's standing there and who's walked away.

There can be a sense of abandonment, a feeling as if everyone has left you behind or forgotten you. That's just another blow when you're coping with a whole new life. Are you angry about it? Sad? Confused? Any and all of the above? Those are normal human responses.

As you deal with the aftermath of a stroke, you must remember that the behavior of others is *not* the fault or issue of you or your survivor. It would be very easy and understandable for you to shut down in anger or self-pity, but survivors and caregivers have to keep opening doors because you never know when someone will step back into your lives again.

As the caregiver, invite, *don't beg*, them to be part of your world. Don't be afraid to say, "We'd love to see you! Do you have time on whatever day? They need to see a face other than mine for a while!"

And that's the truth!

However, don't exert too much emotional and physical energy to keep propping those doors open. Some doors close on their own with a gentle push or the whoosh of the wind. And sadly, some relationships don't survive certain twists and turns in life.

Don't change who *you* are inside to accommodate those who seem insensitive, unwilling to show some compassion or act uninterested in learning about a new life after stroke. Change yourself *only* to seek out new doors that are open, waiting for your arrival and eager to enhance your life.

And that's definitely the truth!

Survivor insight

- ▸ "We have a chance to be teachers. Talk about it. It's very therapeutic. People shy away because they don't know."
- ▸ "When you back away, people back away. When you give, people give."
- ▸ "Sometimes I'm doing better and sometimes I'm not."
- ▸ "My voice doesn't sound anything like it used to."
- ▸ "The more you try, the better it is."
- ▸ "So far stroke is losing the battle with me."
- ▸ "Treat that day as the gift it is."

Abandonment

Looking at his wife, his caregiver, the survivor shakes his head. "Her family deserted her."

After her husband's stroke, she found out on Monday that he would be discharged on Friday, and their house was far from wheelchair accessible. Her sister has a construction company, and the caregiver asked if they could install two handrails and a basic floorboard ramp to get him in and out the front door. Also, there was a small leak in the roof.

Two years later, the sister sent her an unitemized bill for nearly $5,000, and a note, "I thought I'd let you get on your feet before I sent this to you." Stunned, they pulled all they could afford, $750 from their child's college fund, which had already been decimated by the stroke. All their money had gone to pay hospital bills and his ongoing care. They discovered later that the materials in the hefty bill were only a few hundred dollars. The rest was labor.

Soon, her parents were upset that they hadn't yet paid her sister, who was financially well off and had several homes. The caregiver and survivor had already sold everything but their IRA's because of his permanent disability. Arguments erupted at a gathering. The couple wrote her parents and said it was a big misunderstanding. They heard nothing, and that abandonment has left a huge void in her life.

"Make the patient and caregiver aware that relationships are changing," the survivor says.

Yes, stroke can change relationships, some for the better, others for the worse. We can only imagine what's going on in the head of someone who appears to abandon family in the midst of a long-term crisis and challenge, especially something that can be physically, emotionally and financially draining as stroke.

One of the hardest lessons many stroke families learn is that *nothing* can be assumed any longer. You can't assume family and friends will offer assistance, whether physical, emotional or financial without a "price." You can't assume that things will be handled in the same way they would have before the stroke.

What should be expected of a caregiver or survivor? Do you have to issue a formal plea for help if you're struggling? Do you have to beg for assistance from friends and strangers because family has abandoned you?

As caregivers and survivors echo constantly, anybody who hasn't experienced stroke has *no* idea what the real challenges are in everyday life.

That's when family and friends are needed most to help, even in the smallest ways, *not* to question or judge.

And certainly not to send a bill out of the blue.

You, the caregiver, can dwell on "life isn't fair," or you can create your own mottos, based on the following:

▶ Decide not to let others dictate your attitude toward life in a post-stroke world.

▶ Accept that some people will take offense to *anything* you do or say, and you can't change that or them.

▶ Determine your new priorities in life and how important each is to you and your survivor.

The truly important stuff in life will *not* abandon you.

Little BIG insight

▶ Stroke happens to the *family*.

▶ Everybody responds to every situation differently.

▶ Address your worse fears and move on from there.

▶ There may be no greater purpose than bringing someone back to as full a life as possible.

Imperfection

Caregivers, you know you're not perfect, but you're often doing the best you can under difficult and uncertain circumstances. Many are deeply hurt and aggravated when uninvolved relatives or friends butt in or claim the caregiver is *never* doing enough for the survivor.

Says one, "Or they have suggestions for how you could manage. When my husband had a meltdown, people said, *'You need to get right back in his face!'* Well, I tried it once. I won't ever do that again." She laughs seriously. "His brain is wired differently now. In the moment, he may not understand what I'm saying. Many people have told me they'd never put up with what he says at times, but they have *no* clue."

An R.N. who works with stroke patients agrees.

"It's easy to make suggestions." There is no definite answer what a caregiver will face because every case is so different. Unfortunately, with stroke, there can be no predictions or "cookie cutter" solutions or recommendations, she says. That cliché is particularly true here: what works for one may not work for another.

Yet, *no* caregiver has *all* the answers for their survivor. Not even *you*. It's humanly impossible to do everything and do it "right," even when there's no "right way" in certain circumstances. Sometimes we need a fresh perspective from an "outsider," even when it sounds silly or ridiculous.

This is a time when you need to maintain an open mind and/or smile. A sense of humor can be invaluable when ignoring or accepting advice from concerned, yet uninformed, onlookers. Perhaps it can be an impromptu lesson (without preaching on your part) that invites a genuine "I didn't know that" response.

Again, it all boils down to education and drawing upon humor as much as possible when well-meaning, and *not*-so-well-meaning, folks contribute less than two cents. But always keep an open ear, eye and mind out for those valuable dime and quarter thoughts when you least expect.

Survivor insight

▶ "I'm still alive. That's all I ask of my good Lord."

▶ "When I was in the hospital, I had my toothpaste and didn't know what it was for."

▶ "I'm not uncomfortable because I have to live with this."

▶ "Give me feedback."

▶ "(The stroke) made me quit smoking. All the great people I've met through all this, the therapists and survivors, it opened my eyes to all the things I took for granted. I never will again. I got a lot closer to my family and friends, and my faith has really blossomed. I know I can't do the stuff I used to do, but that's okay. I'm just happy to be alive. That's the most important thing to me now." *Survivor*

"I was too weak to pray for myself. I don't even know if I said a prayer. My support was my friends and family praying for me. Now I thank God constantly because I'm not supposed to be here, but He knew different."

Survivor

Differences

Many survivors ask themselves: "Am I different?" That can be scary when they may feel different or not see changes that others witness.

"I try to be the same person. My parents were told to expect me to change," says a female survivor. She asked her dad if she had. He said somewhat, that she was a bit more emotional.

Another says, "The doctors always said I was going to be a different person. I don't know how I've changed. Maybe I do things differently than I did. I try to be calm and not get upset so I don't have another stroke."

A survivor explains, "I really wanted to be the same person after my stroke. That scares the heck out of you. Am I the same person anymore? I really think I am."

One considers herself "definitely" a different person and appreciates the little things in life more. She accepts compliments more easily because she's worked hard at making progress and is glad when someone notices.

Caregivers, keep in mind that some survivors wonder if they can love themselves with what they view as new cracks, chips, flaws and limitations. We all change and evolve over the course of our lives, even though some events can speed up that evolution. We can mature, survive and learn from failures, and seek new challenges when we succeed. We may laugh and cry at different things as we age, even without a stroke.

Survivors need to be reassured that while some things may have changed about them, that the core of who they are hasn't (unless they're a whole lot nicer than before the stroke. It happens!) While some behaviors or abilities may have been altered by the brain injury itself, there is comfort in knowing the "same old me" is still there. Caregivers can help reinforce that message with *sincere* and *genuine* comments.

However, it's okay to note some changes or challenges when the opportunity arises, though never in a negative tone. For example, your survivor may not be smiling as much as they used to. Give them a hug and say, "Your smile makes my day," *not* "I wish you'd smile more." That may be the cue for them to relax and enjoy the subtle treasures of life more.

We all want the freedom and ability to change on *our* terms, but stroke can take that out of our hands, whether you're the survivor or caregiver. Many caregivers have had a lot of changes forced upon them without warning. The only thing we *can* change is our attitude toward ourselves, and the more positive that is, the more you'll appreciate what is so unique about *you*.

Fire

A caregiver says there remains a delicate balance between maintaining a survivor's determination and drive to move forward, yet being realistic about the limitations stroke can impose.

Her survivor mother gets this "fire" occasionally to get up and do things, and daughter and dad have tried to chart her cycle of activity. The mother has unrealistic expectations of her new levels of ability. She now requires naps she didn't before, but she won't take *their* word for it and how the stroke is the cause. After a "meltdown," she goes to the neurologist who explains *again* that it's all part of the stroke. Her brain needs more rest. On top of it all, she fears having another stroke.

It's tough to say, "you can't do this or that anymore," when you're trying to be encouraging at the same time. Stroke can create conflicts within relationships when you're all trying to understand new and frustrating physical and emotional limits, even if they are temporary.

Perhaps a firm, but encouraging, note from the physician or therapist can be posted on the fridge or bedside to remind the survivor that progress takes time and they *are* making improvements. Their body is already working overtime to recover from the effects of the stroke. The message can target a survivor's specific needs, such as how a daily nap will provide a much needed rest and a rejuvenating effect that can put a positive spin on frustrating steps. Make it doctor's orders!

With your help, the survivor might keep a journal or chart to track those naps or other new routines *and* the benefits derived, such as an improved and less anxious disposition. It might also save some doctor trips or at least provide some useful "evidence" of progress.

We can't promise any miracles, but it certainly can't hurt!

Caregiver insight

▸ "I'm frustrated when people ask his prognosis, but we don't know."

▸ "Exercise can affect feelings and helps to process them better."

▸ "Stroke gives a whole new meaning to the word togetherness."

▸ "We're committed to a time schedule. When you're sick before, a couple of days you're better and go on with your life. You want to go on with your life, but it doesn't happen with stroke."

▸ "At first I was a basket case."

▸ "As a caregiver, your emotions are all over the map."

Reality

A survivor, who's a young mother, still struggles with the emotional and physical distance of her teen-age daughter.

"My daughter doesn't like to see me in this state. I think my brother made her come see me in rehab. I think that kids nowadays are self-centered, and they think of themselves and not others. I wouldn't have pictured her that way, but I've been home three weeks, and she hasn't been here."

Her husband, the caregiver and girl's stepfather, acknowledges her sorrow.

"I'm so proud of my wife. As hard as this is, I think she understands that she can only do what she can do, and then her daughter's got to be accountable for her side of it. My wife knows she doesn't need the pressure or the stress. She loves her daughter and will do anything for her to have that relationship, but she can't sacrifice *her* health."

We *never* know how someone will respond to a loved one's health emergency. Family members may quickly unite to draw strength from each other … or step back one by one to avoid the intense emotions the situation can create.

We're human. We don't want to walk into sad situations. We don't go searching for tragedy and grief. However, sometimes we have to look beyond our own emotional pain and how a loved one's stroke has inconvenienced *our* life.

Do some young people today have too many distractions that keep them from facing new realities and responsibilities? Are they self-centered? Selfish? Clueless? Uneducated? Afraid? Combination of any or all of the above?

When do we shield our children and when do we strongly encourage and help them step up? Many young people have been forced into difficult situations and responded incredibly well with a great deal of maturity. A number of children who helped with the caregiving of a parent or grandparent have elected studies and a career in a profession that allows them to assist more families because they understand the challenges firsthand.

Though it's difficult at the time, it's still far easier at a younger age to learn that life isn't always fair.

Anger

A caregiver has witnessed her husband's volatile anger and how it's alienated his family.

"He gets violent if he's not understood. Slams doors, pouts." That can last for a couple of weeks. She has told him a thousand times that his behavior could set off another stroke. He's the oldest of the siblings, but his family is "skittish" on talking to him about his erratic behavior. She wishes he would hear it from another source, not just her again.

If a survivor exhibits anger frequently, that will often put off family who might have been willing to help but now are understandably afraid of agitating the survivor.

That's why it's critical that you educate family and friends on:

- *Why* the survivor is behaving differently.
- *Why* stroke can be the root of this transformation.
- *Why* it takes time for the survivor to adjust to new circumstances.
- *Why* anger is a natural human response to grief and loss that must be worked through.

Anger is a tough issue to address because it's often "contagious" and can make you angry, for perhaps no good reason at all. Think of these:

▸ Is their anger "merely" frustration at the inability to complete tasks or do things independently? Are they too embarrassed to ask for help? Do you need to interject some calm reinforcement and suggest a break?

▸ Is it fueled by short-term memory loss, which can be a stroke side effect? Are they angry because they've forgotten something?

▸ Do certain topics or situations upset them? Look for cues to avoid those completely or find new ways to approach them.

▸ Do they just need a distraction from whatever has upset them? That can defuse many outbursts.

▸ Do they just need to communicate their feelings to somebody?

▸ Do they need some help in addressing their anger? Do they need some reminders or techniques to work through the anger or issue?

▸ Catch them off guard with a hug or kiss or compliment or something funny. It can "stun" them and make them forget the reason for the outburst. It's not being mean to "make" them forget. It's a kindness.

▸ There are times when it's best to allow them to vent, get it out of their system and then move on. We all have moments like that. We're human.

At the same time, how are *you* coping with their anger? Do you take too much of it personally? It's hard not to at times when their rage is or seems to be directed at you. If you're the primary caregiver, you're going to witness it more often than anyone else.

It's a hard lesson to learn, but you have to make sure that someone else's anger, whether it's the survivor or anyone else, does not dictate how you respond in the moment or spend the rest of your day. You have to find the calm within you, the deflector inside, that will fend off anger harmlessly.

You need to find external forces that will make that easier:

▸ Music can calm or energize you in a positive way. Keep a radio, TV, CD or MP3 player handy with favorite music in anger "emergencies."

▸ Look at, walk through or interact with nature. Feed the birds, stroll in the yard, attack the dirt with a shovel in the garden. Mother Nature has some mighty incredible gifts for us to savor when we need some free therapy.

▸ Call a trusted friend or family member who will be your sounding board. Vent your emotions so that everything will become clearer again.

▸ Scream into a pillow or in a room where the survivor can't hear you. When your tantrum is over, think of how ridiculous you looked. Smile.

▸ "I always think about a disk that spins around. If I'm able to talk, fine, I keep on going. But all of a sudden, it quits. I try to say something and can't get it out. I'm not mad but it ticks me off. I'd like to be a little faster. I'd like to talk regular."
Survivor

▸ "People come up to me and start talking. I look at them funny, *'Who are you?'* I feel really bad about it. They understand." *Survivor*

"I feel really rotten because it's like my fuse gets really short. I don't say anything real ugly or hateful. I try really hard to catch myself. I back up and tell them I'm sorry. It's hard."

Survivor

Emotions

A survivor's emotional response to anything and everything may change a little or drastically in the post-stroke world. Some report spells of endless tears and then laughter or vice versa. A kind deed or moderately sad tale may turn them into a waterfall. A childhood joke may send them into convulsing laughter.

Depending on the stroke's location, the brain injury may jumble or exaggerate emotions. The doctor may diagnose certain conditions that explain these behaviors. As the caregiver, you have the challenge of paying attention to these changes and discovering their triggers where possible. Also make sure you don't ridicule what may seem like a childish response.

It's exhausting and frustrating to control out-of-control emotions, even if they're as harmless as laughter or tears. Reassure them it's okay and it's not *them*; it's the stroke. Help them feel more comfortable around others and to create signals or words that indicate they want or need to leave when they experience these difficult emotional moments in public.

Remember, your arms are the strongest safety net in the world.

Depression

Stroke can be depressing in more ways than one.

Many survivors battle depression, a medical condition that can follow a major illness or life-changing event such as stroke. They can experience great sadness as they work through the emotions that accompany stroke. It can be ever harder on those who have aphasia and can't express themselves verbally to talk through what weighs on their mind and heart.

The most important thing is to address it and not disregard their very real feelings. It's appropriate to say, "It's okay to feel this way. A lot of people experience this." Depression can interfere with their recovery if they're not motivated to engage in vital therapy. Don't hesitate to talk to their doctor if it persists. Everybody has down days, but ongoing depression can be a major concern.

And pay attention to warning signs inside *you*. Many caregivers also fall prey to depression, prompted by physical and emotional demands. You're *not* weak if you ask for help. You'll be even stronger because you had the guts to seek assistance. You *will* thank yourself!

Empathy

While he continues to deal with his wife's stroke, a caregiver tells of his sister complaining about her husband's broken leg.

"I was glad to listen to her, but I was thinking, in six or eight weeks, he's going to be back running around. She wasn't being insensitive. She just didn't understand that all the stuff she's talking about I've been doing for five years and will do for however many years are left." It was a big deal to *her*. "It's incumbent upon me to understand where those people are coming from. They're not insensitive or uncaring. They just can't fully realize *my* situation."

A wife says, "Nobody at church has said anything, but sometimes I get the feeling that they wonder why we're not at every activity." They don't "get" all the extra work and time it takes them to just leave the house. "They're never going to understand, but hard feelings will be created if you don't explain. *'I'd love to be there, but I can't do it all anymore.'* "

A caregiver says their adult children have noted, "Dad's got a weird outlook on things now." She reminds them, "Dad doesn't always think about things the same way he used to. His logic is different now. He has a different perspective. Part of that logic is gone now … He can't help it."

One survivor, who had always been independent, told someone she had had a stroke. "They acted like it was a broken leg. I said, *'No, this is a life journey.'* "

A young caregiver says, "I've come across people who know how to see through and read you. It's surprising when you find people who 'get it.' Hang onto those to get you through until you meet the next person to carry you to the next step."

No one understands exactly what anyone else's life experience is like because every human being is different. But feelings can be understood, such as anger, sadness, grief, happiness and relief. Feelings are universal; how each of us processes them is not.

To better educate others about our life situation, sometimes we need to "get" where they're coming from. However, don't wear yourself out in the process. Everyone has their own emotional strengths and weaknesses, some of which seem to make no sense at times to onlookers.

Some people who have always been Hercules are knocked out of their orbit when certain crises arise. Others who were always withdrawn can suddenly stand tall in an emergency.

Yep, it's just another unpredictable quirk of being human.

Consider some of the following:

▸ Spread a little empathy of your own. It's good to get out of your own world occasionally and peer or step into someone else's challenges. You often find others have far more obstacles than you and your survivor have. That can definitely bring everything into perspective.

▸ Some survivors struggle because of isolation, no matter whether it's self-imposed or not. Loneliness can become a feeding ground for self-pity and exaggerated fears.

▸ Many a survivor has been "forced" to do something or go somewhere and then found the experience rewarding because they can connect with the circumstances. Many have thrived by helping others, whether it's other stroke survivors or individuals facing other catastrophic challenges or those in dire financial need.

Empathy goes both ways. We can teach it and learn it.

Caregiver insight

▸ "I've tried to make him feel like he was a person, like he wasn't completely taken over by this stroke."

▸ "Resources are out there, but we're not good at reaching out for them."

Inward

"You definitely go on an inward journey," says a caregiver.

That long and complicated roadmap is littered with potholes, detours and obstacles, but many miles are smooth and provide lots of unexpected scenery when you take the time to glance away from the blacktop surface. That's the only way to see things in the distance in order to slow down to avoid a collision or to witness the beauty that Mother Nature provides.

The journey is an inside job with outside influences. *You* make the decision whether to get angry or let it blow over when your loved one asks you the same thing for the 100th time or criticizes every turn you make at the car steering wheel. Remember, it's the stroke, not the person … unless they've *always* been that way …

▸ Find ways to keep your cool. Count to a number that keeps you focused, recite calming poetry or sing in silence to your favorite tune.

▸ Frequently resort to friendly humor, which can quickly ease a tense situation. That's much easier to do than repair hurt feelings, especially in someone experiencing cognitive challenges from the stroke.

▶ Challenge yourself to look for the good in what seems like an impossible situation. It's lurking in there somewhere when we truly open our eyes and take the time to look.

▶ Give yourself a break from unrealistic, self-imposed expectations. Nobody's perfect, including you.

We wrestle with many emotions during life-changing or threatening experiences. They're not always easy to sort and prioritize. Love and fear are often considered two of the greatest motivators in life and can bring out the best and worst in us. Sometimes love can exaggerate our fears, and fear can cloud our love.

No, it's not easy being human, but it's the one gift we all unwrap at our own pace. And sometimes it's okay to rip that paper to see what's inside.

Caregiver insight

▶ "I've learned how to ask for help."

▶ "His personality is so positive. We've lived life."

▶ "Though we've lost a lot of friends, we've gained probably more loving and understanding friends."

▶ "Sometimes we get so caught up in the caregiver role that we forget to back off and let things be."

Grief

An adult daughter misses the "old" mom's insight and motherly advice that flowed before the stroke.

"She was always saying exactly the right thing." Her voice breaks as tears fall. "It's just different now. It's not her fault. When you guys miss your spouses, the dancing, I miss my mom."

"I'd miss my mom, too," a fellow caregiver reassures her.

"In a way," she continues, "it's cool to read the e-mails she used to write, but in a way it's sad."

"Now *you're* the mother."

Relationships are priceless no matter their level as each is completely different. There are unique bonds between spouses, parent and child, siblings and friends, and there are challenges when stroke injures one of the principals in that partnership. Caregivers, family members and friends miss the "old" person, all the fragile pieces that make each of us unique and special.

There is grief after a stroke. "Something" has died, even though the survivor is still with us. Maybe they've lost certain cognitive or physical abilities, or their emotions are jumbled in confusion, at least early on. What was once automatic now requires concentration and extra energy.

Mourning is not over in the usual three-day absence most employers give someone when they lose a loved one. Despite our desire for grief to unfold in a neat little package and be done with, it doesn't work that way. Individual hearts break and heal at different rates.

We can't define anyone else's love or say ours is better. It is ours alone to protect and nurture. The bond of love is truly beyond words because it defines something much deeper. Love ignites many emotions, and loss or change can rattle us at our very core and promote unexpected fears.

Yet, the aftermath of stroke can create new levels of love and longing within us that we didn't know existed. We miss someone who's still there, the familiarity of their voice or touch, how they would bring us gifts or groceries, make us laugh or do our laundry.

We make many assumptions in life, that loved ones will be there tomorrow, that they'll remember everything about *us*. That is why stroke survivors and caregivers constantly repeat this refrain: *NEVER take life or loved ones for granted.*

Yes, you will bear some level of grief after your loved one's stroke, but there is always hope, just waiting for you to reach out and grasp it.

Don't wring your hands. Open them.

"You didn't die, but you kinda did. The you that you know died. You kind of say goodbye to yourself. It's so upsetting though I still count my blessings."

Survivor

▸ "My husband doesn't like to watch me struggle. I tell him, *'It's best for me, it's good for me. If you can't watch me, go outside. You can check on me, but let me do it.'* " Survivor

▸ "I still have days where I cry, but that's okay. For me it's better to laugh than cry. I don't let myself stay in that place very long. My friend says, *'You're the only person I know, I come to you for a pity party and you let me have two minutes and that's it!'* " Survivor

Listen

The 60-something survivor explains the challenges he faced when coping with aphasia in the years immediately following his stroke.

"When you're not able to talk, that's really bad. I didn't know if everybody was the same. I was going to the gym. I had to go to a speech person … therapist. They helped me start to talk. It was still really hard. I was doing enough that I could go to the gym, but somebody had to pick me up. I knew a lot of people there, but I didn't say too much because I couldn't talk too much.

"A lady knew what I wanted to say. It got a little easier each time. I started talking with more people and felt more comfortable about it."

Communication can be one of the greatest post-stroke challenges, depending on what part of the brain was affected. A survivor may have trouble with receptive or expressive aphasia or other disorder that affects incoming and/or outgoing speech or comprehension. Aphasia is an impairment of language, affecting the production or comprehension of speech and the ability to read or write.

Disruption in communication is one of the most aggravating, depressing and misunderstood side effects of a stroke. It requires the most patience as it may keep a survivor from expressing themselves or from being understood on the simplest of requests.

For the short or long term, it requires constant practice and reinforcement. You, the caregiver, carry a huge load in maintaining that neverending classroom, but that can be tiring at times when you just don't feel like talking or listening. We all need breaks! We all need quiet time!

There are talkers and listeners in this world, and it's worth the effort to find them to help a survivor learn to engage in trivial, yet vital, conversation again. The listener may be a neighbor, friend, or someone else you engage with frequently. There are people hungry for interaction! You can find at least *one* person who can be *the* audience the survivor needs to regain their voice and courage when you need a break.

That therapy is *free*. Embrace it!

Survivor insight

▸ "Don't tell me I can't do something; enable me to do it."
▸ "If you tell some people they'll never do something, they don't have the empowerment to try anyway."

Ask

If a survivor experiences aphasia, responds slower than before, has some cognitive difficulty, or is hard to understand, people often quickly shy away, or simply give up and immediately search for the caregiver to "interpret."

Many onlookers wrongly assume that if a survivor exhibits any of the above, that they can't comprehend much of anything.

A caregiver says, "He's sitting next to me. It really irritates the heck out of me if people ask *me* if *he* wants something. He's sitting right there! Ask him! It's so frustrating. They're adults, not children, although they're dependent."

Another wife says, "We'd gone to my parents for breakfast, and they said, *'Does he want toast?'* Ask him! He's right here! They felt uncomfortable."

Just because they may be dependent on someone for physical care doesn't mean they can't be part of an activity as an *individual*. It's crucial to a survivor's emotional well-being and physical recovery to be recognized with conversation, eye contact and/or touch.

Survivors can teach us the beauty of the art of listening. It takes patience and time, but it is worth every second because it enriches *your* mind and soul. If we truly want to be heard, we must take our turn at listening. How else will we know what to ask and answer?

All that stroke survivors and caregivers ask is that people give survivors the precious gift of a few minutes to find out how they're *really* doing. That simple interaction can transform your day in a positive way. Encourage family and friends to communicate with your survivor. People often don't know what to do or say. Help them with cheat sheets or pep talks or a list of cues that make everyone feel more comfortable. Tell them:

▸ Look them in the eye while interacting. Avoid distractions.

▸ Don't automatically complete their sentences or thoughts. Practice will be the best teacher on when to help and when to be quiet. Even if they have some difficulty, most survivors can respond to questions in some way, gesturing, verbally, nodding, writing, etc.

▸ Don't just say "uh huh." Be specific when responding by offering follow-up statements such as, "I like that store, too," or "It sounds like you had a fun day at the park."

▸ Be patient and don't look at a watch or clock. Survivors who struggle with word expression will feel rushed and then may become frustrated, which will hamper their efforts even more.

Here's the basic rule in life: when you ask somebody, "How are you doing?" *say it like you mean it*, and be prepared to hear their response. You can meet the most fascinating people that way, because their answers can enlighten, educate and/or entertain you in some way.

Being ignored is painful, no matter the circumstances, because that promotes social isolation at the time the survivor needs to be connected with the rest of the world the most. *You* have the power to break down invisible walls that imprison your survivor. *You* have the key!

Survivor insight

▸ "Even though I'm in control of most everything, the stroke is still a major setback."

▸ "It took a while. It was my new life. It was deal with it or just sit and die."

▸ "There is always a tomorrow."

▸ "Going slow isn't so bad."

▸ "I had seven doctors. None of them ever looked at or talked to me. They'd talk to my wife. That's the problem. They never get together and talk with each other (about me). *'What's wrong? What's going on here?'*"

Engaged

The caregiver smiles at her husband, who sits in silence next to her. He fully understands every word she reveals, though he cannot convey them himself.

Because of severe aphasia, he's lost the ability to speak more than a few words or engage in ordinary conversations. What does she want the world to know about strokes?

"I want people to be more understanding. I have girlfriends; we don't have couples. They think you can just pick up and go, but you can't. I also find that they don't want me to talk about it. They'll ask, *'How is he?'* They want a sentence and no more. That hurts so much. I'll listen to what they have to say, but they don't want to hear what *I* have to say. I've gotten to the point where, *'He's fine.'* "

Those words evoke great sadness. It's a cry for one of the most basic human interactions, the act of being heard. We need to talk. We need to listen. It's a continuous circle of communication that educates and engages us in everyday life.

Here's the big question for you, the caregiver: who's listening to *you*?

▸ Who will absorb what you have to say without judging you?

▸ Who will engage you in a healthy conversation that helps you answer some of your own questions?

▸ Who will help you turn on your own light bulbs of awareness and understanding?

▸ Who will offer advice and *not* a lecture?

▸ Who will lift, cheer and entertain you when that's all you need?

Start making your list and checking it twice, because you're going to eliminate the naughty and keep only the nice.

Survivor insight

▸ "Use common sense."

▸ "You can't change the world, but you can change what you do."

▸ "We're survivors, not victims."

▸ "What I learned is that you can get better if you work at it. I never thought I'd be able to dress myself or walk with a cane as I can now."

Forward

"What can you do? What can you say?" asks a three-time stroke survivor. "Sure, I've cried. Nothing I can do. Three's not a reason to be mad at the Lord. I've learned to ask for directions and not be afraid. If you're handicapped, people feel sorry for you, but I don't want them to. A lot of people are worse off than me. Still makes me feel bad.

"I want people to be honest with me. Don't lie. Be honest and fair. I'm on disability now and used to be a good employee, but it's not easy. I try to stop and smell the fresh fruit. I've made mistakes but can't change the past."

That's one of the truths of life that we all need to accept, especially stroke survivors and caregivers: *you can't change the past*. Stroke truly alters our prepared and predictable life script and gives us almost too much time to think about the past as we also ponder our future.

There can be amends, apologies and lessons learned from our mistakes. Fear of death or a drastically altered life can bring out the best and worst in each of us.

The aftermath of a stroke is not a time of blame, though it is a period of grief, a natural response to the losses a stroke brings, complete with stages of anger, bargaining and the bombardment of intense emotions. We are blessed and perplexed by complex human feelings.

Ask yourself these most important questions:

▸ How can I truly move on and forget a past I cannot change?

▸ What lessons can I learn from and build upon without guilt?

▸ How can I become a better person in response to this incredible challenge I've been handed?

▸ How can I turn grief and disappointment into something positive?

▸ How can I help others based on what I have learned?

We all have to do a lot of soul-searching as we set aside the past and decide that we *do* have a say on our future. Therein lies the hope and limitless possibilities. Turn off the past and turn on the future.

Caregiver insight

▸ "A year is nothing in the life of a stroke."

▸ "I had missions and goals, more than concerns."

▸ "There are some things that are the way they are."

Summarize

A caregiver explains that her survivor husband looks "fine," but his receptive aphasia is worse than expressive. He will have put on a "great act" during a medical appointment, but when they get in the car, he asks what the doctor said. She's learned to practice a concise and simple summary for the rerun.

Because of the brain injury, he may unintentionally tell someone something wrong only because he couldn't understand what was originally said or his interpretation was incorrect. She says he often transposes numbers in conversation or is off by $100 or $1,000 when quoting a price. That's led to several startling conversations with friends and family. She laughs as she says *she* keeps the checkbook.

As the caregiver, you need to pay attention to the little and big things survivors do and say:

▶ Tune into their comprehension level, which can be affected after stroke.

▶ Pay attention to how they describe events you both attended. Are they confused about what really happened, yet seem confident of the details? Even downright adamant and stubborn about it, even though they're wrong? Decide how important it really is to argue about it.

▸ Do periodic checks of their short-term memory. See how accurate their recollections are of today's, yesterday's and last week's happenings without "interrogating" them. Make it a casual conversation. Have them help *you* "remember."

▸ The more attuned you are to their memory and comprehension range, the more prepared you are to fill in details where necessary.

Think of a summary as giving mini book reports without worrying about being graded!

Little BIG insight

▸ Many survivors become more emotional after the stroke, and it takes time to learn how to balance those feelings.

▸ Laughter can salvage a bad day.

▸ You have to take charge and be an advocate for the survivor.

▸ A survivor's loss of hearing is tiresome as family members don't want to shout but sometimes they have to. You may have to consider a hearing aid.

Vocabulary

A caregiver saw a sign, "tree trimming ahead," and asked her husband if he could read it. He said, "Cut 'em up pretty soon." He couldn't say the specific words but he knew what they meant. Most of the time he's correct, but surprisingly, it's often hardest with little words like "a," "the," "and" or short proper nouns and names. He wrote "Bob," but it didn't look right. He couldn't come up with the word "buffet" but said it was a place where "all ready and pay for it."

Well, you know what, that's okay because he "gets it." It's exercising a part of his brain that the rest of the world often lets go dormant. It's actually creative. And by golly, a buffet *is* a place that's all ready and you pay for it!

Remember the following:

▸ Words may literally take on a whole new meaning after stroke.

▸ Clichés may be lost in translation in a post-stroke brain.

▸ Look for signs of puzzlement or confusion and take time to explain.

Listen to your survivor. You may learn a new vocabulary word or a description that you have always taken for granted.

▸ "My wife and kids mistook me and were getting all on me until I explained myself, then it was all okay. My wife calls it a filter. After my stroke, I didn't have a filter. Whatever went through my head came right out my mouth. Sometimes it wasn't pleasant. But everybody knew where I stood. That's come back. Now I'm able to think before I speak and not hurt people. I used to be misunderstood a lot. I meant good but it came out all wrong. That was our biggest problem. The way I think about it and the way they think about it was two different ways. I could speak but it would get all messed up in my head." *Survivor*

"I was pushed from the very beginning and encouraged to do it myself. But there are times when I can't. It's frustrating when they say I can do it by myself and I know I can't."

Survivor

Tough

A man describes how his mom had a *really* bad day. She got confused while driving, hit a car and then later crashed into a telephone pole. It was thought she had a mild stroke, and losing her driving privileges "just about killed her," he says.

Then she had two strokes in a short period of time. Placed on medication, she went to therapy and regained the strength in her affected arm, though her leg still had problems. The biggest challenge for her was having to be dependent for some everyday needs, but it actually enhanced her life because of the outpouring of support from family and friends.

He says his mom is a very practical person. She was given a choice: sit all day and do nothing, or work to improve and continue doing many things for herself. She wants to stay in her own house as long as possible, and she's doing it because of her commitment to improvement. For her, it's more a case of being able to do the things she wants to do and seriously addressing her new challenges. The stroke "toughened Mom up" to do things she didn't think she could do, he says.

While some survivors may feel like failures if they're unable to complete a specific challenge at first, many actually thrive when told they can get to work or just sit all day instead. Is it reverse psychology? Maybe. Maybe not. Determination and stubbornness can create quite an amazing team.

Anger and frustration can also be quite powerful motivators. Haven't you wanted to say, "Fine, I don't care. Do whatever you want. It's your life." Many a caregiver has left the room and returned to find the survivor doing whatever they had refused to do earlier.

We walk that proverbial fine line of tough love, encouragement and rubbing raw emotional wounds that defy healing under pressure. Every individual is motivated by different rewards, realities and dreams.

And just when you've figured it out, it can all change on a whim. That's part of stroke and human nature as a whole.

At least give them something unbreakable to throw. It's good exercise.

Survivor insight

▶ "Stroke has many meanings. All but one means something positive. Attack, you can't think of anything that is positive."

▶ "It's not that you're stupid."

▶ "It's like ... they don't listen. It's like ... you speak another language."

Humor

One family told the survivor that he looked like Jesus Christ when he took his hair out of his ponytail. One day he walked into a fast-food restaurant with the grandkids and said that he was Jesus Christ, meaning it as a joke. His wife tried to explain to him that while it's funny to the family, it may not be to other people.

He has trouble filtering at times, she says, but she lets him go on his own most of the time because "he doesn't do weird things." A sense of humor helps tremendously.

"He misses the fact that people don't talk to him." He needs to be around people, but she doesn't want them to make fun of him. She wants to encourage them to try again.

Tell folks to give the survivor a break! He just wants to interact with old friends and new ones, and savor the sound of voices, including his own, filling the air again. Stroke can be very isolating, and we all need human connections to be part of the world.

Stroke survivors crave laughter and a chance to share the intimacy of humor with loved ones and friends. Laughter is very personal and reveals much about what tickles us on the surface and deep inside.

Humor also exercises the brain by forcing it to connect the complex array of cells that make us giggle or guffaw. You don't have to be a stand-up comic to exhibit a sense of humor. You don't even have to be able to stand up! Humor comes from an open heart and healing brain.

Laugh with survivors, *not at them*, and you'll both find some genuine joy in everyday life. Many survivors have learned to appreciate life at a basic, uncomplicated level again, and all of us could benefit from that refreshing view.

And laughter is much, much cheaper than therapy!

Caregiver insight

▸ "She has nothing in her control."

▸ "We blame it on the stroke."

▸ "I'm not the same person I was when we first met. I've changed."

▸ "We have to beat the system."

▸ "I know I have to grieve eventually, but I keep myself so busy and wrapped up in other things. I don't allow myself time to relax and do something else."

Repeat

During a visit, a family member saw the survivor successfully raise her affected leg three or four inches off the ground and lower it. That was quite an accomplishment, but the visitor decided to have some fun.

"Oh, I didn't see that," she said, in a totally innocent voice.

The survivor played along. With a smile, she repeated the motion.

Isn't that just a little more enticing than, "Lift that leg"?

Different fuels motivate us when we don't want to do something or struggle with the task awaiting us. That's just being human. Survivors battle even greater challenges, and we can lift that emotional load significantly by adopting some new game plans along the way.

▸ Challenge the survivor by saying, "Nah, you can't do that."

▸ Say "Don't you do that!" in a playful tone. That often has the desired effect in encouraging them to do just the opposite.

▸ Use bribery whenever and wherever possible. Make it fun!

And just like the shampoo bottle says: shampoo, rinse and repeat. Only this time: smile, challenge and repeat.

Investment

The caregiver shakes her head.

"When something goes wrong around our house, like when the water heater breaks, it's *my* problem." With water in the basement, she's back and forth between work and home waiting on the plumber.

Her husband can't report what exactly happened with the plumber if he's there by himself, and she gets frustrated. She has to call and say, "My husband is a stroke survivor. Can you please tell me what you told him because he can't explain it to me?" She goes back to her husband and informs him that they said *this, not that,* and it's more expensive. "He'll say, *'Let's do it anyway.'* I say, *'No, that costs money.'* "

Keep the following in mind when you're trying to balance all those concerns in keeping the household running:

▶ For everyone's safety, know who you're dealing with when you have to schedule appointments and can't be there yourself. Consult only with reputable service providers that you've worked with before or have been referred to by friends or family. Check them out.

▸ If the survivor honestly cannot handle financial matters or make important household decisions solo, notify any service representatives *ahead* of time before they show up the house that they'll be working out details with you. Have them put estimates in writing and/or call you directly, and make sure they treat the survivor with respect and gratitude.

▸ Explain the matter as simply as possible to the survivor and why the option you're leaning toward makes sense, is the best for the family or costs less. Discussing it reinforces the decision and gives the survivor a voice and chance to ask questions, some of which may influence the decision in a positive way. Don't count them out completely!

In reality, there are some decisions that the caregiver must make alone in the interests of safety, time and finances, but there can and *should* be opportunities for survivor and caregiver to make choices together. The caregiver has to remember how left out, hurt and "worthless" *they* would feel if they suddenly had zero say on the big and little decisions that are part of a family's everyday life.

The "investment" of time you make together today will pay many unexpected dividends in the long term, especially in bolstering a survivor's self-esteem and reinforcing that they are still a vital part of this family. You never know what great ideas or solutions may be just waiting within them that can brighten your world and lighten your load.

Classroom

The caregiver has her hands full of groceries and a wet umbrella, and the empty-handed survivor stands there impatiently waiting for her to open the door. Normally she does open the door, but this time obviously can't. "I can't do it. You've done it before." "No, I haven't." So, they'll stand there arguing until he does or she drops everything to do it herself.

This situation is darn aggravating for a caregiver who can easily and understandably forget that the stroke may have injured the part of the brain that ignites and controls common sense and social cues. It's a disruption in routine and not an automatic response for this survivor. He's used to doing it by himself when he's alone, but it's *her* job to do when they're together. Believe it or not, that's a whole new routine.

Practice is how many survivors relearn things. It may take minutes, hours or weeks to teach them something old that's new again. The caregiver has to fight the temptation to blurt in frustration, "You know how to do this!"

Every movement, decision and action is controlled by the brain. If familiar paths are injured or destroyed by the stroke, the brain has to create new pathways to relearn what the rest of the world takes for granted.

▸ Make this a new responsibility that is taught and committed to memory. That way, it doesn't come across as a chore or "sudden" inconvenience to the survivor. Remember to thank them with sincerity.

▸ Practice being the one carrying something so they can be the one who opens the door, an action that will give them confidence in this new role. Be the one who hands them the groceries to put away as they relearn the way the kitchen is arranged.

▸ Slowly introduce new situations, keeping in mind your survivor's ability to adapt and their frustration threshold … plus your own.

It requires patience, which is one of the greatest attributes a caregiver must adopt, and it isn't a skill learned in a day. Many a caregiver has defused an "explosion" by reminding themselves that the next time will be easier and faster. This is the *only* way to promote independence in this classroom of life.

Just remember to schedule class when the caregiver's arms aren't overloaded … and it's not raining.

"The hardest thing is the evaporation of people who just don't show up for the long haul. It's all immediate. 'We're with you. We're praying for you …' Then they go on with their own lives. That's the hardest thing to deal with without being bitter."

Caregiver

▸ "The doctor said we could write *the* book. I don't want to write *the* book. I want him to tell me what to do for my brother. He said, *'He's a miracle. You should be happy with that.'* Okay. Miracle. Now let's get down to telling me what else I can do because he's going to be around another 25 or 30 years, and he doesn't want to sit on his duff for that long." *Caregiver*

Checklist

A survivor tells his caregiver, "You should check me better!"

He was mad because he couldn't find something he thought he had packed for a trip. He searched everywhere but became more irate by the minute. His caregiver tried to calm him and help him search. She quickly found it. He had just overlooked it in his self-imposed rush and anger.

None of us wants to be judged or "graded" by someone standing there checking off everything we do or don't do. That's an embarrassing and stressful situation the survivor shouldn't have to add to their worry list.

Do you add "check everything the survivor does" to *your* to-do list? Some survivors will think you're babying them, hovering or don't trust them, and will be resentful. Remember, it may be one of those times when you just can't win. Accept it and move on!

▸ When traveling, caregivers do need to doublecheck to make sure vital medicines and favorite personal items are not forgotten. Say, "Here's *our* checklist to make sure that I/we don't forget anything." Don't use "you."

▸ Make "the" list lighthearted and offer the survivor a chance for input on it. Maybe it's a master list you create together once and not have to reinvent every time. It can be modified over time.

▸ Or hide the list from them to ease what they may perceive as unwarranted stress.

And no matter how organized you are, also be prepared to take the blame if *they* can't *immediately* find something. Their anger often erupts out of fear or panic that everything they need to function in a strange environment isn't there. A stroke may alter their ability to quickly adapt.

It's a sense of losing control of yet another segment of their life if everything isn't *exactly* where it needs to be for their ease. That may be just part of the stroke's effects. If you understand the reason behind the "attack," it makes it easier for you to respond and not take it quite so personally.

And this will keep everyone in check!

Survivor insight

▸ "I may not do a very good job at it, but I try."
▸ "I know what I want to say but I can't get the word out."
▸ "I like being around people."
▸ "Stroke is just a second chance … a new normal."

Recognition

A caregiver tells others that the hardest part is that her younger sister writes down everything good about her life and what *other* people do for her. However, the caregiver does everything and receives not a single "thank you."

"I do all this stuff and it's not appreciated. I feel empty and dead inside. Her big sis is just a pile of crap."

She's been taking care of her in her own home or else the survivor would end up in a nursing home "where she'd wither away. I had no choice."

One time she helped the survivor to the floor during a seizure, and the survivor got bruised in the process. A nurse asked what had happened, and the survivor blamed her sister, even though she had saved her from more serious harm.

Someone tells this caregiver that she needs to remind herself that she's a good person. The woman says she tells herself that, "but somewhere I died."

A fellow caregiver says, "You don't get recognition. You've got to pat yourself on your back."

Another says survivors expect an awful lot.

"But it doesn't make it right."

Caregivers should realize and accept right now that caregiving is often a thankless job or responsibility. While there are many survivors who do say please and thank you, others do not. Some survivors are wrapped up only in themselves, whether out of self-pity, a lack of etiquette recognition or retraining, anger, or other factors due to the brain injury. Or some may be just totally selfish. Period.

▸ If your survivor can say please and thank *others*, they are capable of doing the same to you, their caregiver. They shouldn't save all their frustration and anger for just you, while giving the rest of the world a smile.

▸ Revert to childhood manners training. When they say, "Get me something," respond, "And what do you say?" They may look at you oddly because you've caught them off guard. Sometimes, that's what it takes to rejuvenate the brain cells in charge of etiquette.

▸ Put up some gold stars or other items that mark your achievements. Leave those stickers in a convenient place for the survivor to recognize you, too.

Most human beings give without expecting anything in return. Of course, we all beam or blush with a simple thanks. It does a body, mind and soul good, so don't hesitate to thank *yourself*. Good job!

Discovery

"Nobody knows how to do this," says a male caregiver. "Today the survivor can be okay, but tomorrow they're not. Often it's hour to hour. You have absolutely no idea what's ahead. How can you really prepare for the next phase, good or bad?"

Unfortunately, you can't. The ultimate track shoe to keep up with some survivors' needs hasn't been invented yet. However, caregivers can maintain a sense of humor, allow an abundance of flexibility, establish meaningful routines and schedules, and learn to accept all the colors in the spectrum because there's no black and white in stroke or caregiving.

Because every case is different, study your survivor's new life history that is being written by the minute, after an initial rush of chapters composed in the earliest weeks and months. There are patterns of behavior, responses and emotions you should commit to memory or at least paper. You'll discover patterns of behavior *and* progress that can provide some valuable insight and predictability.

No, you can't read a survivor's mind, but you can better understand their actions, responses, accomplishments and fears. If you don't, it can drive you crazy and dampen your sense of humor and adventure.

Yes, there are moments of "I wish I could make this easier for them" or even, "Here we go again!" That's the reality of stroke. That's human nature.

You can better accommodate some major events and minor blips simply by paying attention to words, reactions and body language. You learn over time that there are certain situations to avoid and positive challenges to tackle. You just have to remember the victories and learn from the defeats as you discover new ways to set your survivor up for success.

Caregiver insight

▸ "I'm the mean daughter."

▸ "We've come through a lot."

▸ "As soon as you show him what needs to be done, he does fine. He has more trouble with verbal instructions."

▸ "My temperament level is not what it used to be."

▸ "There are tiny miracles every day."

▸ "We've turned a stroke into a blessing."

Purpose

A CNA describes how her neighbor, a relatively young stroke survivor, was living for a time in a nursing home, surrounded by elderly people. It took a harsh emotional toll on him, being around seriously ill patients who would likely live out their days there.

She faced challenges of her own after losing her husband and ended up becoming this survivor's caregiver to keep him in a home environment.

"We had that same hurt. Right next door. Not a second thought, I should be doing this. He's trying to be happy and dealing with the life he's been dealt."

Survivors need to be needed, too, because it give their lives purpose and meaning. We all need to be needed and to share our unique gifts, even when we fail to give ourselves much credit. We easily lose faith in our abilities when we are sick, tired, depressed or only see our deficits when we look in the mirror. We question our strengths and overly fixate on our weaknesses, which can lead to an intense and debilitating self-defeating attitude.

Often we can lift ourselves by helping others. We can forget or set aside our own emotional and physical pain when we reach out to someone else who's suffering or struggling. We can touch others in ways we can't begin to imagine, all by taking the risk of opening our heart or door.

▸ Get involved in a stroke support group. Your successes, even if they seem small, will inspire other families coping with stroke.

▸ Work with your local stroke center and offer to come in and meet with families new to this brain attack. Offer insight and hope.

▸ Attend charitable events. There are many no-or-low cost events in your community that will educate and entertain you.

▸ Write cards or letters to shut-ins.

▸ Check with local social agencies to see if they need help. Some survivors are unable to return to a full-time job, but they can still put their talents and time to good use for others. Or do it together.

Survivor insight

▸ "You've got to celebrate the littlest thing because it's big."

▸ "Focusing on others than myself makes me feel better."

▸ "The more you try, the better it is."

▸ "There are a lot of things you can do that you think you can't do."

Needs

A caregiver describes how her husband's sister, a retired teacher, lives nearby and has been stepping on their toes ever since his stroke.

"We need a sister, not a teacher," the caregiver says.

Sis talks to him like he's a child and often brings a list of words for him to learn that day. They need a sister, someone who will talk to him about what's going on in and outside his world and simply interact "normally" with him.

"He understands. Don't talk to him like a child. She's missed so much. She wants to be in charge, but there's not enough room for everybody to be in charge. She also smokes. I'm trying to understand her, but I don't have time for that."

Family or friends who barge or waltz in and have "all" the answers can create ill feelings because they're usually spending more time talking and correcting than listening and learning. Is this a way of masking their own insecurities and fears? Or is it just being plain old rude and/or clueless?

Many people who thrive on listening to their own voice and opinions may be that way because they know only what *they're* going to say. However, they can't control what someone else, especially the survivor or caregiver, may say or ask. Maybe they have a need to control something, *anything*, since they were powerless to stop the stroke and its devastation.

Or, maybe it's time you worked up the courage and politely, though firmly, said, "We don't need a teacher today; we need a sister." Catch them off-guard with a smile and embrace that *you* control. Or tell them it's okay to be afraid of the changes they've witnessed but not to be scared anymore.

"Let's make the most of this new life together. He needs his sister. I need you, too."

Decide what you have to lose and what you could gain by speaking up. That might shut them up in more ways than one.

Little BIG insight

▸ Survivors may grasp the options they have but need help making decisions. Or maybe they can't process all the choices.

▸ It's frustrating to a survivor when they can't understand why they tire so easily. It's the brain injury.

▸ Caregiving is not just sitting. It's movement, it's encouragement, it's involving other people, it's love.

▸ "They can still do many things they did before, but everything takes more time. Learn to add in some extra time when going somewhere or doing something." *Caregiver*

▸ "Encourage, encourage, ENCOURAGE! Let them do for themselves or figure out a logistical way THEY can do it! Make adaptations to aid independence, such as change chairs. Add chairs, use bars and railings, use liquid soap vs. bar soap. Change whatever has to be changed so they can do it themselves!" *Caregiver*

"There are lots of generous and loving people out there just waiting to help out or get information for you that may be helpful. Stay as involved as possible in social areas of your life so you do not become secluded."

Caregiver

Acceptance

A woman describes how her husband broke down sobbing after he discovered he could no longer change a tire ... a skill that he had mastered years ago as part of the male ritual of learning to drive and routine car maintenance.

Yes, it's a "guy thing."

However, his expression of deep sadness is part of the grief process and accepting loss, and it's okay. He's a stroke survivor, and this is one of those "moments of truth" a survivor must face periodically and work through. It is also a reminder of just how amazing his progress has been since that horrifying day of the brain attack, and what skills and abilities he has reclaimed or reshaped to better fit his new life.

A survivor must recognize new limits and opportunities. Is a woman no longer a "real woman" because she can't perform certain household duties that were once her domain? Is a man no longer a "real man" if he can't perform certain chores that were once his domain ... like change a tire? Absolutely not!

Bless the "grown" man who cries! He's administering a deep cleansing of his soul. He will see himself and the world clearer when his tears dry.

We need the losses to better understand and appreciate the wins. That's not only a valuable credo for survivors but for all of us. If we do not fail occasionally, we will not learn how to savor the true value of success. That's why survivors may need some extra encouragement at times to remind them they're only a few steps from the next achievement …

Like *asking* for and *accepting* help to change that tire.

Caregiver insight

- ▶ "I have no one to blame but me to do some of the things that I really want to do."

- ▶ "When I hear someone else's problems, I think I've got it pretty good."

- ▶ "Are my behaviors giving a message I don't want? Am I complaining about things I shouldn't?"

- ▶ "It sounds so simple to make a plan to get help but hard to put it together."

- ▶ "I need to show him that somebody else could care for him. I'm proving to him that if something happens to me, he can go on with someone else."

Routine

The brain repairs itself every second of every day, and some lessons must be taught again and again. Yes, they may be relearning things that they perfected as a child, but the survivor is *NOT* a child ... unless they happen to be in that chronological age bracket.

Many caregivers report that when they take the time to teach the survivor a new routine, it makes a *tremendous* difference in remembering steps and getting everyday chores and challenges accomplished. If you don't want to take the time to work with them now, be prepared to do even *more* later when you're rushed or impatient. Then it's likely going to be a disaster ... or least result in hurt feelings on both sides.

Now, here's the possible drawback: once some survivors learn a routine, they may not easily budge when something different comes up. For example, when you travel, the survivor will likely need to set up everything in the unfamiliar bathroom the way it is at home, and if you try to mess with that, you may get a nasty or flustered response ... which can be totally justified if the survivor feels forced into adapting too quickly.

The best way to combat that is have some *ir*regular or practice days at home. Explain that you're going to rehearse for the vacation or trip so that they'll feel more comfortable when they arrive. Ask them how they'd like to pack their belongings. Is there a favorite suitcase? Is that old piece of luggage so big that it now overwhelms the survivor? Do you need to get a new one that is smaller and more compartmentalized to help them make it their own?

On the vacation or visit, you may need to adjust routines to fit into other people's schedules as much as possible. This can be an opportunity to educate the survivor on others' needs if they still have difficulty looking at a situation from another perspective.

Little BIG insight

▸ Stroke really tests the patience of everyone involved.

▸ Survivors are ignored most when people can't understand them.

▸ We all deal with days when we're tired, and it's easy for anybody to complain, including survivors.

▸ Yes, some days, living with a stroke or a survivor seems like a downtrodden country song.

Choices

Formal therapy doesn't last forever. Dollars and time run out, but survivors must continue to push themselves for the rest of their lives to improve and not lose what they've regained.

A speech pathologist explains, "The brain is the slowest organ to heal. That's why it's so important to exercise the brain because it will try to find ways to work. If you quit, your brain quits. If you quit trying, your brain quits trying. It's important to have a good attitude and keep trying new things, even though it's scary."

A 40-something female survivor says: "I try all the time, but I don't have the finger pinch to hold a pen or pencil with my right hand. For the first year after my stroke, I refused to write with my left hand. Now as a goal, I'm starting to practice with my left hand. I realize that the right hand, if it comes back, great, but I need to write legibly. I try to practice a little every day, but it's one of those winter things to do when I can't get outside."

"You lose so much," says another young survivor. "You're an individual used to doing for yourself. You find yourself in the shower with three or four therapists teaching you how to shower. If you're modest, you can't do that anymore. It's hard."

A male survivor remembers, "When I told someone I spent 80 percent of my day in a wheelchair, that was unfathomable for him. So I asked myself, *'Why do I spend so much time in a wheelchair? I don't know.'* One day at a time, I gradually became more active, getting out, driving for a purpose."

Consider the following:

▸ Fighting the urge to give up should top the survivor's priority list for life. Yes, there are going to be days when they're simply too tired emotionally and/or physically. Caregivers have to be vigilant, but not nags. We all need a day or two off, but survivors can't afford a bunch in a row. The brain demands consistency to function at new peaks of performance.

▸ Focus on an incentive plan, positive reinforcement, humor and even reverse psychology to keep a survivor motivated. Many survivors admit that they regret slacking off because it slowed their progress. They had to stick to working hard to truly enjoy the benefits.

▸ Yes, the most dramatic progress will be made in the early weeks and months, but maintaining a schedule is crucial for life because there *will* be those unexpected miracles all along the way.

Social

A survivor says stroke gave her a whole new reality.

"I had the stroke. You forget about the world in a sense. Then you're starting to see that the world goes on."

A group of doctors' wives took patients out to lunch each week. She was invited to go. Her mother encouraged her.

"I said, *'No, no, I can't do that! A lot of my friends don't know I had a stroke and that I'm in a wheelchair.'* That's what I thought about. I had never sat in a wheelchair, and here I am, I couldn't do anything else but sit in a wheelchair. *'I haven't gotten in touch with my friends. I can't go out into public like this.'* The lady told me, *'You seem so cooperative. You do everything the therapists ask. You'll be going home soon. Why don't you at least experience this so you can have something else to share.'* With her putting it like that, I thought, *'Why not?'* "

The woman told her she'd be riding a bus with a chair lift, and it would be a good experience.

"I had *the* best time. That was when I first sensed that I would enjoy a social life again. I'm going to be me again. Before my stroke, I loved going out to dinner with friends and co-workers. That's me. We talked so much that I forgot I was in a wheelchair. I started to feel better. The following week, they asked if I wanted to go. Oh yes! Life goes on."

▸ Most stroke survivors or anybody can sense pity immediately, so steer clear of it!

▸ "Sell" a new challenge or experience as fun, entertaining or a chance to be "normal" or "one of the gang." Maybe it's something the survivor has feared doing alone or in a crowd and can now attempt in a "safe" environment.

▸ It's so important to pay attention to what a survivor does and does *not* communicate. Find those opportunities early and often!

Despite our attempts at times, life does go on, stroke or no stroke, ready or not. There's no hiding from it. But the real world may be just the prescription we need to discover and/or create our new seat at the table of life.

Little BIG insight

▸ If a survivor takes one extra step every day, imagine how far they'll get in six months physically *and* emotionally.

▸ Sometimes the caregiver needs more help than the survivor.

Flexibility

A caregiver tells of speaking to a group about stroke, and how she and her survivor husband needed to make a few last-minute changes.

"We have this banter. We had practiced. But he can't adapt quickly, though he usually goes with the flow."

She announced to the audience, " *'I brought a show and tell.'* He looks at me and smiles. *'I got ph-phasis. That means I can't always spit it out. I'm going to tell a story. She helps me when I can't spit it out.'* He gets through one and then stuck in the second story. *'What do I want to say?'* I say it. He says, *'That's what I want to say, and I think that's our story.'* "

They got a standing ovation.

"We have to adapt for the environment. You don't know what's going to happen, and luckily, he rolls with the punches."

Even with all the planning in the world, life can be and is unpredictable. When you're coping with stroke, there are going to be diversions and changes that come along every day or hour. It's vital to adopt a positive attitude of facing a new adventure, instead of bemoaning mistakes or coulda-shoulda-woulda.

The necessary evil of adaption is one of the many nasty by-products of stroke. It may be forced, but it can be accepted with acknowledgment and an attitude of making it work. Adapting can be a way of making a difficult situation easier to bear or a little less uncomfortable.

Throw the need for perfection out the window now!

You always needs contingencies, a backup plan or route. Face it, very few things go according to plan. That's just the way life is.

Relax and look for the humor or special memory in the situation because it's lurking there somewhere. Get over it and move on!

Survivor insight

▶ "I'm doing fine. It's everybody else with the problem."
▶ "Getting outside is great because it gets your whole body moving."
▶ "I want to say it so bad but can't say it though."
▶ "It is what it is."
▶ "It's so frustrating that I can't control what comes out of my mouth."
▶ "I refuse to give up."
▶ "The speech therapists did too good of a job. Now I never shut up!"

"One doctor told me I'd have seizures the rest of my life because of the stroke. Another doctor told me the seizures would decrease as the brain heals itself. The second doctor was right. God made your body to heal itself."

Survivor

▸ "I worked hard to become independent. The more confident you become, the more confident (caregivers) become … I have to remember how to do this." *Survivor*

▸ "I'm able to talk better all the time. I don't know if I talk to people more. I think it helps me to listen to what everybody else says. My brain thinks more and more. If I sit there and watch TV, I won't be able to talk at all." *Survivor*

Reasons

Survivors get tired of hearing about stroke, stroke, stroke, stroke …
"It happened. If I have to hear about stroke again …"
"After 400 times, you don't want to hear about it."
They don't want to be reminded of "it." Please ask them how *they're* doing, but refrain from using the "s" word all the time. People don't want to be identified solely by the "s." They want to be regarded as an individual, as a human being, a man or a woman, a girl or a boy, not as the person who had the "s."

Generally, avoid the following:

▸ Talking about other people you know that had a stroke and how well or badly they're functioning now. Every stroke is different. Acknowledge this survivor's unique challenges and opportunities.

▸ Saying, "You look great!" unless they really *really* do.

▸ Reciting, "Things happen for a reason." Stay clear of it. Honestly, the survivor is the *only* one who has permission to express that theory.

One caregiver shakes her head at how many relatives and friends said about her husband, "He's such a nice guy. Why would God make him have a stroke?" "A lot of people think that. I say, *'God didn't do it, but God helps us through that.'*"

Speculation about God's "motives" is best kept to yourself or shared in private with your religious or spiritual leader.

A survivor says, "I think I'm stronger than I gave myself credit for. In some ways I'm myself and better. Like I told our pastor, I may not be the sharpest knife in the box, but I've grown within. My relationships with people won't be the same. I lived life from the fullest anyway, but I know what a gift it is. People that worry, they're missing out. We can't take advantage of our time. I hope that I'm an inspiration for people. I have to believe that that's God's plan."

Let the survivor say that if *they* want. If you agree, great, but don't preach about it. If you don't, then get it over it, because it's *not* about you.

Survivor insight

▸ "I'm here. I didn't think I was gonna be."

▸ "Sometimes God has given me something before I even needed it. I'm going where I'm meant to be."

Familiarity

One survivor announces with a smile, "If nobody moves it, I can make it work."

After a stroke, that's *not* the time to move everything around as a survivor relearns the household again. Of course, you may need to move things aside to make more room for the survivor to get through if they're now using a wheelchair, walker or cane. Or you may need to lower or raise some items in the bathroom or kitchen so they can easier reach them.

Well-meaning family members or friends have come in to clean or organize and instead create new headaches for both survivor and caregiver. Survivors have often said that their whole world has been jumbled by the stroke, and they long for their own little corner at home that *hasn't* changed.

At home from the hospital or in-patient rehab, reacquaint the survivor with the layout of home, but don't continually ask, "Do you remember this?" The priority is that they're safe and feel comfortable. Go room by room and see what they can reach and need to learn to navigate and indicate what is where. Some adjustments will likely be necessary, so do them together so that you both can take ownership.

Maybe this is the time to do some necessary or desired remodeling to make the new living arrangements work better for everyone. Perhaps this is something a friend or family member would love to assist with, a gift they can give from their heart and hands, *as long as the changes meet the caregiver and survivor's tastes and requirements.* Surprise remodelings often backfire.

Because of the difficulty in reaching an upstairs bedroom, many families have moved that room to the main floor. The survivor's unique needs may dictate whether they need their own bed. For couples, the survivor's sleeping habits may have changed so much that they need separate beds, such as restlessness that would disturb the caregiver, who also needs their rest, or the addition of railings to keep the survivor from falling out of bed.

That requires an emotional adjustment, too, particularly for couples who've slept together for decades. Many do make it work, some by putting twin beds together or moving from a full or queen size to a king to give a little more space for everyone's comfort, and more importantly, to keep them close.

Keep the following suggestions in mind:

▶ No matter how weathered or outdated their easy chair is, *leave it alone* unless there is a medical reason to get another one, such as a chair that lifts to make it easier for them to get up by themselves.

- Keep favorite blankets, pillows or other items out and easy to find.

- Condense the number of remote controls and stick to the one that is the easiest for them to operate.

- Keep favorite movies or music out in view for easy access.

- Keep nearby favorite books, magazines or newspaper. They may not want to read or be able to comprehend the printed words anymore, but they may enjoy looking at photos of favorite activities.

- Don't be surprised or upset if they go through drawers or closets looking for specific objects. Put things back together and don't expect them to remember exactly what went where.

Survivor insight

- "If laughter was a medicine, I'd be well by now."

- "It's frustrating not being able to work. I've pretty much lost most of my life. I lost my marriage, my kids. But I have more than some people have; I'm taking care of myself."

- "I was kicked out (of therapy) a year and a half ago."

- "Nobody says they graduated from therapy."

Technology

A speech pathologist notes the challenges of introducing computer therapy programs to older survivors who have little or no technical experience:

"My generation grew up with computers, but I'm also working with the generation that is having strokes in their 60s, 70s and 80s, many of whom never worked on computers. I might describe a therapy program that would be great for them, but if they've never worked on a computer and don't own one, that's a problem.

"It's how we transition from the old way of doing things to using those components of therapy for recovery. That's a hard transition when you're dealing with such a broad range of people's ability levels, what they're used to. A 40-year-old and a 70-year-old, one has used a computer and one hasn't, you're going to do completely different things with them."

And here's where patient children and grandchildren can find a special calling to help with therapy lessons at home. Maybe they can be the ones who get the basic computer up and running and keep the survivor on task with homework. Plus, they might find just the right games to add more fun to the experience. They need to introduce this very beneficial therapy and make the survivor feel comfortable with it, not intimidated or threatened.

Research has shown that many survivors of all ages benefit from the repetitive and interactive programs available today on devices of all sizes, from handheld to desktop computers. Survivors have enhanced their reading, speech, communication and reasoning skills with practice. This may be the most cost-effective approach to keeping survivors engaged and learning when formal therapy ends.

Keeping the injured brain active and focused via computer programs is *not* a waste of time when they're trying to regain skills. It also promotes fine motor exercises and hand-eye coordination.

It can also be a new road to communicating with loved ones via email and online chats, but in text and video. Use available technology to keep opening doors to the world that awaits the survivor.

Survivor insight

▸ "I keep saying that I'll get on the computer, but I'm always messing around with something else."

▸ "You've got to really watch when you research stuff online. A lot of it is a hill of beans."

III

Protective

The discussion leader poses a delicate topic to the survivors:

"Are your caregivers worried about you too much? Caregivers go through this fear of almost losing you, and it's easy to become over-protective. But how can you retrain your brain if you're not allowed to try or fail? Yes, it is easier to just jump in and do something for someone. But you can use opportunities to try. Even if you fail, you get an A+ for trying. Does the caregiver always know what is best for the survivor?"

Most of them immediately shake their heads. We'll take that as a *NO* with comments such as:

"Don't talk to us like children."

"I understand things. I can't talk well, but I can understand everything."

Well, here's what some caregivers say:

"Sometimes he's unaware of the consequences and acts like a 20 year old instead of being an 80 year old," a wife says. "I try to be his cheerleader to do anything by himself. I guess sometimes I am protective. I caught him outdoors with a tall ladder above a cement patio trying to clean the gutters." She shakes her head at that dangerous scenario.

"My situation is a bit different than the usual," says another. "He recovered so well that he was able to resume his part-time job. Then he had several falls, the worst resulting in a broken collar bone and a head wound. These falls took their toll on his physical being, and he was never able to get back to the place that he was in before it happened."

This is a tough topic. One of the greatest fears a caregiver has is leaving their survivor unattended because of health concerns, which could be anything from choking to falling. They may be unable to speak and call for help if left alone. No wonder caregivers are scared to death on many occasions.

But caregivers or, in fact, *no one* individual can keep an eye on someone 24/7. It *will kill* you to have that responsibility, the stress alone, which is mind-boggling. You need helpers, human and technological if there is a valid need to make sure someone is available around-the-clock.

Some survivors have railed at their caregivers for bringing in "babysitters." In fact, some survivors refuse to let anyone else in. Sometimes, a survivor's fears, justified and not, can be selfish and dangerous.

However, one husband went a bit overboard in trying to protect his wife, who was fully ambulatory and cognitive of her surroundings and activities. The survivor remembers the feeling of being trapped inside her own home while being left alone:

"He took the keys away … no house key, nothing. I thought, *'But what am I going to do if I walk out of the house?'* I said a house key maybe."

This is a topic with no one "right" answer. It all depends on the circumstances of each survivor. There's a huge difference between being careless or irresponsible and "what if-ing" yourself to death.

This is a topic that survivors and caregivers *must* visit often because a survivor's disabilities and abilities change and evolve. Though the survivor is not a child — unless they are agewise — this is a similar situation that parents and children go through as a child becomes more independent.

With stroke, it's not only a matter of trust, but one of memory, education, honest communication, routine, and plans of action in case of an emergency. Survivors have to understand and work within and on their limitations, and caregivers have to learn to let go and give the survivor the independence they crave and have shown they can handle.

Do caregivers *always* know what is best for their survivors? Sorry, not always. A heavy mixture of fear and love may cloud the best of intentions and create a feeling of being over-protective, or what the survivor may deem as suffocating. What may have seemed the right thing to do at the time, really wasn't as it didn't take into consideration the survivor's feelings and reality of their progress.

Travel that journey hand-in-hand. Learn when to let go. *It will be okay!*

▶ "Medical personnel don't have the time to tell you how to live this new life. Get into a stroke support group or two or three. Go to activities. We live in a country that fortunately has lots of handicapped accessible places. Talk to others who are living this new life. Each one will be different, but you can take advice that applies to you. Get on every mailing list for aphasia and physical therapy so that you can continually be aware of new things to help you. Prioritize your life. Your loved one is more important than dusting the house. Accept where you are, hope for what may improve and value each day." *Caregiver*

"It'll be okay, but you have to encourage them. You can't get frustrated because we have no idea how frustrated they have to be trying to figure out what's going on. Encouragement always, patience, love and support make all the difference in the world!"

Caregiver

Victory

"Newer" caregivers often feel guilty or frustrated that they can't do more for their survivor. There are natural ebbs and tides of feeling useful and useless when you can't control or rectify certain situations.

More often than not, you, as a caregiver, need to learn when to step back and just let the survivor do something on their own, even if you're certain they're going to "fail."

The word "failure" takes on a whole new meaning after stroke. What may be described as failure to 99 percent of the population, may be an incredible victory for a survivor. If the world cheered survivors' accomplishments as much as able-bodied, highly paid athletic performers, just imagine the thunderous roar! That would wake up the world to what victory *really* means.

Where is that fine line of doing too much or doing nothing? Some survivors say their caregivers won't allow them to try anything. "How am I ever going to get this back if they won't allow me to do anything?" Safety is a consideration, but ... (see story on "Protective.")

▸ Many survivors will try something a million times if it means they can walk or talk or read or write or do *something* normally again. Many fight for every word or step or object to grasp with reawakening fingers. And sometimes they need to do it alone to vent their frustration to themselves. And that means the caregiver, you, just need to walk away and let them do it.

▸ There's a difference between suffering and struggling. Yes, help them if they're suffering, but if they're struggling with a goal and have focus and determination, leave 'em alone! Unless they specifically ask you to stay and cheer them on. Not too many do.

▸ Sometimes *you* may be *the* distraction. When their every move is not being devoured by a caregiver's eyes, they may blossom in ways you can't imagine. How would you like somebody watching *you* all day? Kind of a suffocating thought, isn't it?

Humans were created to be independence of one another, yet dependent. Learn when the time's right for each. Set the alarm for success!

Survivor insight

▸ "I've learned to let go of the past and look forward to the future."

▸ "I still can't believe that your brain makes you so tired."

Zip

A caregiver says, "Friends told me he'd say more if I'd shut up." Everyone laughs because they understand.

Caregivers, do you talk *too* much? Do you speak up for your survivor before they'd had a chance to form a response? Do they give up before even trying because they know you're going to do all the talking anyway?

Know right now that medical personnel deeply appreciate the caregiver being there if the survivor has aphasia or other communication difficulties. However, don't automatically speak for the survivor at the doctor's or the diner or wherever you go together.

You may think they don't have much or anything to say, but maybe you just haven't given them the chance. Today may be the day that they really have a great story or sentence to share. Today's the day they may have perfected a joke they've been practicing in secret for weeks. Today may be the moment when a song bursts from their lips.

They may need longer to break into the conversation than the 1-second breath you've taken in your monologue. Sometimes you need to zip it.

Junk

In their frustration to rid of what they may view as junk, some survivors go on cleaning sprees when caregivers least expect or are *not* in the mood for purging. The following example is repeated in many stroke households.

"I came home from work," says a wife, "to find he'd completely emptied the linen closet. He was ranting about (and back then, he could really, *really* rant) too many towels and 'shit,' and his command was that I 'get rid of it,' meaning everything HE didn't think we needed. He pointed to things he didn't remember ever seeing.

"I took the less conflicting path and told him that a relative made the crocheted throw when I had back surgery. I remember being so touched by her making it and being wrapped in it while I recovered, so I needed to keep it for *me*.

"So, he began to see that there was a reason for much of it. Once I put about six old towels in a bag to use for rags and threw away the empty toilet bowl bottle, he was better, and I put it all back. It took my entire evening, and I remember thinking that I needed to help him understand a bit about his actions, not be mad at him, a worthless emotion in that moment.

"The next episode was the same thing, only everything from under the kitchen sink. He didn't know what I needed with all the potions there. Once again, I sucked it up, threw a couple of things away and reorganized them, and he was okay. Things *do* get better, and I love reminders of how far we've come!"

Someone's treasure is another person's junk, and that can be magnified after stroke. Recovery is an "inside job" with much of a survivor's focus on getting better, which is what we all want. However, some survivors do not understand the importance or sentimental value of some items to other members of the household, and need gentle reminders that the survivor is not the only resident with personal possessions.

If your survivor seems agitated by the contents of a closet, drawer or box, take the time to go through it together and do some cleaning and organizing at the same time. The way things are arranged may need to be altered to help promote more independence for the survivor.

The opportunity to do "something" may ease the frustrations created by their new limitations. They may be physically mobile, but may not be able to return to work, which can prompt boredom or feeling useless. Those survivors who stay home while the caregiver returns to work may want to help in some way, though may be unaware of the consequences of their altruistic actions.

One caregiver discovered that her survivor husband had thrown away her mother's wedding china. It was in a box, and he got rid of it in an effort to help his wife after her mother's death.

We can't fully grasp what is happening under the surface after stroke. The brain injury may cloud common sense, empathy and/or memory. The pre-stroke brain knew how much his wife treasured that wedding china, but the post-stroke brain did not.

What can you do? Be proactive instead of reactive wherever you can by being observant and in tune with what may be their cleaning moods. There are no guarantees, but you can always mark important boxes with big red stickers that scream "STOP!"

Caregiver insight

▶ "Eight years ago, I got over this romanticized view of him recovering."

▶ "Our lives are different than we expected, but doesn't mean it's a bad life."

▶ "I need to put a little bit of intention in my life vs. what has to be done."

▶ "It's the hardest job I've ever had, caregiving."

Motivation

While some caregivers are kept hopping by overly active survivors, others may have survivors who are physically able, yet refuse to do anything around the house. That can create resentment and frustration, especially for caregivers who have to work outside the home to provide income to sustain the family.

Even survivors with limited use of one side of their body can do much with their "good" side. Routine chores are practical exercises and vital contributions to keep the household running. Survivors often feel useful and worthwhile when they assist with laundry, dishes, cleaning, etc. It is excellent and *free* therapy to rebuild cognitive and physical abilities, and many report it was the best route to regaining life skills.

However, there are some who sit and do nothing all day long, even though they promised they'd do chores while the caregiver is at work. At the end of the day, a tired caregiver returns to find unwashed dishes and laundry, etc., which often sets off emotional fireworks that puts more distance between them.

Caregivers have to try to look at the situation calmly and get to the root(s) of "why" by examining the following:

▸ Did they not understand the directions?

▸ Do they feel like they're being asked to do too much?

▸ Are they afraid of trying something on their own?

▸ Are they afraid of asking for help and appearing more "disabled"?

▸ Do they need a "pep talk" to get moving?

▸ What motivates them now, compared to life before stroke?

▸ Are they overwhelmed by depression?

They have sustained a brain injury, and this can radically affect emotional responses to even the most mundane daily activities. Many survivors battle depression in the weeks and months following the stroke, and some struggle with fear of failure before they even attempt something that used to be automatic before the brain attack. Depression is a very real illness that can be treated in a variety of ways, so get medical help.

When that has been ruled out or treated, then take the time to discover what will now motivate a survivor. Do they feel like they're being ordered around? Do they think you're not sympathetic to their unique challenges? Do they have trouble expressing their frustrations and feelings, which is then exhibited in being uncooperative or defiant?

Survivors and caregivers *have* to communicate and can assume *nothing*. Both parties are unsure what the other is thinking on many occasions, and that creates misunderstandings and discomfort, which is detrimental to a relationship. Both have to be equals in many respects, even if the survivor needs more assistance and the caregiver takes on more responsibilities. There is still much you can give each other, when you better understand how each other "ticks" in this new life you're sharing.

Discover what will motivate and inspire each of you *now,* a process that will certainly enlighten and may even surprise you. Learn how to work together as a team, as partners, each contributing something unique to strengthen your relationship in ways you didn't know were possible.

Survivor insight

▸ "Our bodies do a lot of changing after the stroke."

▸ "I don't even think about having another stroke."

▸ "All of our normals have changed."

▸ "Know why we did those dumb and stupid things? To have something to talk about when we get older."

▸ "I had some good news this week. The neurologist released me forever!"

Positive

A positive attitude is crucial and mandatory to surviving the physical and emotional challenges of stroke, says a survivor, two years after her brain attack.

"You can't be negative at all. Thank God I'm alive! I *can* do this and this and this. Don't look at what you can't do anymore because that's not going to change anything. It's what you *can* do, your strengths, and be positive about it. That's probably the biggest thing to where I am now.

"Yeah, I still can't drive, I can't work, I can't stand more than a minute or two. I have to rely on family and friends to go anywhere. I used to always be going, doing things with friends. I used to visit my sister every three weeks. I hadn't been to visit her in maybe five months." She admits that she broke down one day, upset that she couldn't visit her sister because everyone was busy. It was a down time.

"But very seldom am I down (about the stroke). Instead it's been a whole new opportunity to do things." Now she's knitting like crazy, making items for needy individuals, something she never did before. And there are many more things to celebrate.

"I was so proud of myself! I went down the stairs, and I went up the steps. Granted, everybody was whizzing by me, but I made it up eight steps. *I was happy!* I would have never done that before. I walked around downtown New York City … I was able to do all that. Granted, I couldn't climb all those stairs at the Statue of Liberty, but I never looked at that. Hey, I walked around the entire Statue of Liberty! Every time I'd go someplace, I would be like, *'Do you know what I did!'* That's a big thing."

This survivor's attitude is right on target by stressing that everyone, including the caregiver, needs to focus on what is positive and possible and steer away from negative emotions and thoughts. Research and common sense shows over and over again that a positive attitude is the most effective weapon we have.

▸ Despite how "bad" you and your survivor have it, there is *always* someone out there facing greater challenges that you can begin to imagine. A positive attitude saves time, money, and emotional and physical energy.

▸ Discover what inspires you and your survivor. What makes you both smile and laugh? What radiates sunshine on the rainiest day? Begin a list of your mutual blessings, and that alone will prompt even more.

▸ Give yourself the gift of a positive attitude, and you *will* change and lift the world at the same time.

"They don't understand that we have seen something they haven't. Stroke becomes a bond between us. We learn things in trying to survive. We've learned to slow down and think and understand."

Survivor

▸ "Not much has happened in my life since my stroke. But the best thing is how well I've rehabilitated and how fast. Here I am. I'm kicking butt at all of them." *Survivor*

▸ "I know that I can work to help others, too. I know I can ... some way I feel like I can teach someone." *Survivor*

▸ "Just because you've had a stroke, doesn't mean you're out." *Survivor*

Resources

Just a few of the MANY websites related to stroke:

American Stroke Association
www.strokeassociation.org

National Stroke Association
www.stroke.org

www.strokenetwork.org

www.strokecamp.org

www.strokessuck.com

www.aphasia.org

www.aphasiawtx.org

www.caregiver.com

www.caregiving.org

www.strokecopebook.com

Monica Vest Wheeler

A former weekly newspaper reporter and editor, Monica Vest Wheeler creates books and materials that focus on human relationships, personalities and history, and sharing her passion for these topics with the world.

She started her business in 1992 and has researched and written 10 Peoria, Illinois, area history books. In addition to co-authoring a book on coping with cancer, Monica has written *Alzheimer's, Dementia & Memory Loss: Straight Talk for Families & Caregivers*, one of the books in her *Help Me Cope & Survive!* series. Her latest projects in the series focus on coping with the daily challenges of stroke, brain injuries and brain tumors-brain cancer, also featured in the *Answers to Everyday Challenges* line of books.

Monica has spent thousands of hours working with and interviewing and listening to hundreds of patients/survivors, families and caregivers, and healthcare professionals. She's given dozens of presentations on writing, the need to communicate, ways to express emotions on paper and verbally, how to use family history to better understand oneself and family today, and ways to cope with the emotions of catastrophic injuries, illnesses and diseases, and much more.

She lives in Peoria with her husband, Roger and cat, Lois. They have a son, Gordo.

To contact Monica for speaking engagements at workshops and conferences on any of the aforementioned topics, contact her at: 877-COPING-0 (877-267-4640), strokecopebook.com, monicavestwheeler.com, info@copeandsurvive.com, or P.O. Box 276, Peoria, IL 61650-0276.